Horizons

Mathematics 3

Book 1

MW01000387

by
Sareta A. Cummins

Edited by
David J. Korecki

Illustrated by
Tye A. Rausch

Editorial Assistant
Christine A. Korecki

Revisions
Alan Christopherson
Chris Burkholder

Alpha Omega Publications, Inc.
Rock Rapids, IA

Horizons
Mathematics 3

Horizons Mathematics 3, Book 1 is only a *part* of a mathematics curriculum which consists of Horizons Mathematics 3, Book 1; Horizons Mathematics 3, Book 2; and Horizons Mathematics 3 Teacher's Guide. It is *necessary* to use the Teacher's Guide for a complete third grade mathematics program. The Teacher's Guide contains some essential concepts that are not presented in the student workbooks.

Horizons Mathematics 3, Book 1
Copyright © MCMXCIII by Alpha Omega Publications, Inc.®
804 N. 2nd Ave. E., Rock Rapids, IA 51246-1759

Printed in the United States of America
ISBN 978-1-58095-963-6

① Write the numbers in standard form.

three thousand, eight hundred sixty-one

_____ = _____ thousands + ____ hundreds + __ tens + __ ones

five thousand, six hundred eight

_____ = _____ thousands + ____ hundreds + __ tens + __ ones

nine thousand, four hundred twenty-seven

_____ = _____ thousands + ____ hundreds + __ tens + __ ones

two thousand, thirty-five

_____ = _____ thousands + ____ hundreds + __ tens + __ ones

six thousand, five hundred forty-nine

_____ = _____ thousands + ____ hundreds + __ tens + __ ones

② Write the addition facts having a sum of:

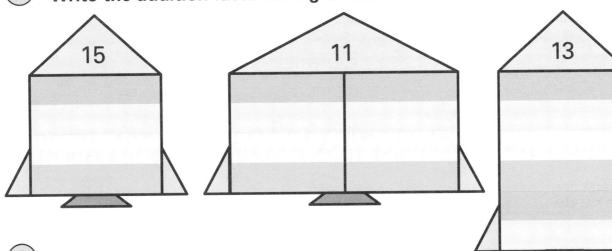

15   11   13

③ Write the correct letters in the blanks.

,

__ __ __   __ __ __   __ __ __   __ __ __ __

__ __ __ __   __ __ __ __ __

5 th — O	16th — Y	13th — H	6 th — M	10th — S
19th — R	2 nd — L	18th — A	17th — E	3 rd — L
8 th — B	14th — I	1 st — I	4 th — D	12th — T
15th — S	7 th — Y	9 th — E	11th — T	

1

④ Find the sum.

13 + 27	58 + 38	36 + 45	64 + 18	27 + 36	45 + 27	39 + 58	29 + 23
42 + 48	14 + 57	36 + 28	29 + 66	35 + 36	57 + 18	68 + 25	79 + 12

⑤ Connect the dots.

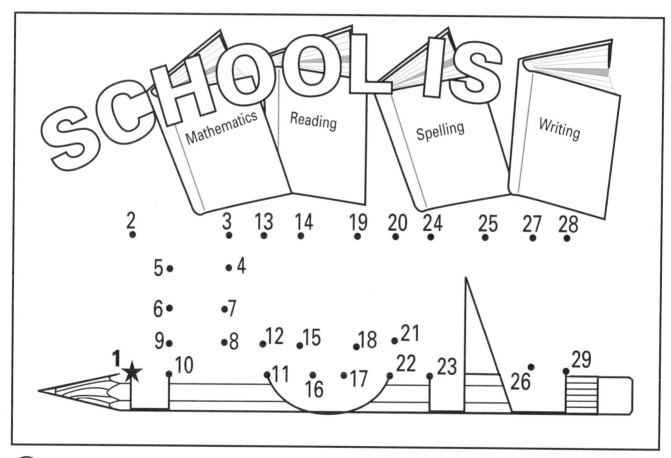

⑥ Find the difference.

79 - 69	53 - 51	68 - 20	94 - 30	95 - 84	37 - 27	86 - 25	73 - 43
48 - 21	65 - 12	94 - 61	56 - 34	82 - 30	69 - 37	27 - 15	87 - 62

(1) Match the numbers.

23rd	fortieth	483	three hundred twenty-seven
86th	seventy-fifth	609	six hundred ninety
40th	twenty-third	572	five hundred seventy-two
57th	eighty-sixth	327	four hundred eighty-three
31st	ninety-second	690	eight hundred thirty-eight
75th	fifty-seventh	838	six hundred nine
92nd	thirty-first	250	two hundred fifty

(2) Write the numbers in expanded and standard form.

four thousand, three hundred twenty-five

4 thousands + 3 hundreds + 2 tens + 5 ones = _____ + ____ + __ + __ = _____

seven thousand, two hundred six

7 thousands + 2 hundreds + 0 tens + 6 ones = _____ + ____ + __ + __ = _____

one thousand, eight hundred forty-three

1 thousand + 8 hundreds + 4 tens + 3 ones = _____ + ____ + __ + __ = _____

eight thousand, seventy-one

8 thousands + 0 hundreds + 7 tens + 1 one = _____ + ____ + __ + __ = _____

five thousand, six hundred ninety-two

5 thousands + 6 hundreds + 9 tens + 2 ones = _____ + ____ + __ + __ = _____

(3) Find the sum.

84	98	80	94	73	61	82	53
+ 90	+ 11	+ 23	+ 75	+ 56	+ 97	+ 45	+ 51

92	62	81	86	72	67	94	81
+ 50	+ 47	+ 34	+ 73	+ 34	+ 60	+ 31	+ 66

3

4 **Find the difference.**

89	76	78	58	63	94	18	45
- 85	- 36	- 56	- 17	- 22	- 24	- 15	- 23

96	89	47	99	74	82	69	57
- 73	- 30	- 31	- 49	- 61	- 42	- 41	- 50

5 **Write the subtraction facts having a difference of:**

6

Across

1. 74 + 83
4. 6 hundreds + 4 tens + 7 ones
7. 6 tens
9. 70 - 50
10. three hundred seven
11. 65 - 10
13. 2 tens + 4 ones
15. 98 + 46
16. eight hundred fifty-one

Down

1. 59 - 43
2. 32 +   18
5. 4 tens + 2 ones

6. 7 tens
8. 5 hundreds
11. 5 tens + 1 one

12. 32 + 22
13. twenty-five
14. 87 - 46

4

(1) Circle the closer ten.

29	20	30
32	30	40
86	80	90
51	50	60
97	90	100
48	40	50
73	70	80
14	10	20

38	30	40
92	90	100
63	60	70
84	80	90
77	70	80
59	50	60
41	40	50
16	10	20

(2) Write the correct time.

_____ _____ _____ _____ _____

_____ _____ _____ _____ _____

During the morning the time is (A.M. or P.M.)? _____

During the afternoon the time is (A.M. or P.M.)? _____

(3) Find the sum.

81	67	86	96	45	53	42	98
+ 49	+ 89	+ 84	+ 47	+ 75	+ 68	+ 68	+ 76

73	57	76	28	97	89	87	53
+ 59	+ 93	+ 86	+ 95	+ 87	+ 23	+ 94	+ 77

4. Write the numbers in standard form.

two thousand, three hundred fifty-eight
2 thousands + 3 hundreds + 5 tens + 8 ones = _____

six thousand, seven hundred four
6 thousands + 7 hundreds + 0 tens + 4 ones = _____

nine thousand, one hundred ninety
9 thousands + 1 hundred + 9 tens + 0 ones = _____

five thousand, eight hundred twenty-seven
5 thousands + 8 hundreds + 2 tens + 7 ones = _____

three thousand, sixty-nine
3 thousands + 0 hundreds + 6 tens + 9 ones = _____

5. Match the numbers.

484	four hundred eighty		408	four hundred forty-four
480	eight hundred forty		880	eight hundred forty-eight
804	eight hundred eighty-four		440	four hundred eight
844	four hundred eighty-four		444	eight hundred eighty-eight
840	four hundred four		848	eight hundred eighty
448	eight hundred forty-four		488	eight hundred eight
404	eight hundred four		888	four hundred eighty-eight
884	four hundred forty-eight		808	four hundred forty

6. Find the difference.

87	49	28	87	37	28	59	95
- 17	- 48	- 14	- 54	- 12	- 22	- 43	- 42

73	86	76	94	58	19	69	98
- 13	- 85	- 36	- 53	- 17	- 16	- 12	- 10

1 **Write the numbers.**

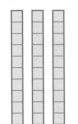 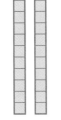

3 tens + 2 ones = 2 tens + 12 ones

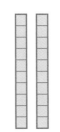 

___ tens + ___ ones = ___ tens + ___ ones

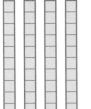

___ tens + ___ ones = ___ tens + ___ ones

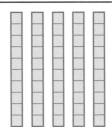 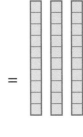

___ tens + ___ ones = ___ tens + ___ ones

2 **Write the numbers.**

63 falls between 60 and ____.   46 falls between 40 and ____.

87 falls between 80 and ____.   22 falls between 20 and ____.

39 falls between 30 and ____.   58 falls between 50 and ____.

71 falls between 70 and ____.   14 falls between 10 and ____.

3 **Write the correct time.**

_____   _____

_____   _____   _____   _____   _____

During the morning the time is (A.M. or P.M.)? _____
During the evening the time is (A.M. or P.M.)? _____

7

(4) Write the numbers.

3,286 has a ___ in the tens' place.

3,286 has a ___ in the thousands' place.

3,286 has a ___ in the ones' place.

3,286 has a ___ in the hundreds' place.

7,490 has a ___ in the ones' place.

7,490 has a ___ in the hundreds' place.

7,490 has a ___ in the tens' place.

7,490 has a ___ in the thousands' place.

(5) Find the sum and write it as a word number.

```
  59
+ 43
```
_____

```
  75
+ 86
```
_____

```
  37
+ 93
```
_____

(6) Jonathan and David were catching butterflies. Jonathan had 7 butterflies and David had 16. Who caught the most butterflies? _____ How many more? ____ How many butterflies did the boys catch together? ____ _____

Rick rode the elevator up to the 18th floor in a hotel. Next he wanted to ride down to the 5th floor. How many floors will he go down? ____ _____ What is the 8th floor above the 16th floor? ____ _____ What is the 7th floor below the 14th floor? ____ _____

1 **Write the value of the blue digit.**

3,864 _____   4,382 _____

7,259 _____   5,196 _____

1,603 _____   6,728 _____

8,475 _____   3,541 _____

2,910 _____   8,267 _____

2 **Write the correct time.**

_____   _____   _____   _____   _____

_____   _____   _____   _____   _____

When I am finished with school the time is (A.M. or P.M.)? _____

When I eat breakfast the time is (A.M. or P.M.)? _____

3 **Write the numbers.**

36 = 2 tens + ___ ones   42 = ___ tens + 12 ones

74 = 6 tens + ___ ones   83 = ___ tens + 13 ones

51 = 4 tens + ___ ones   19 = ___ tens + 19 ones

98 = 8 tens + ___ ones   67 = ___ tens + 17 ones

25 = 1 tens + ___ ones   50 = ___ tens + 10 ones

(4) **Write the numbers.**

37 falls between ____ and 40 and is closer to ____

42 falls between ____ and 50 and is closer to ____

96 falls between ____ and 100 and is closer to ____

84 falls between ____ and 90 and is closer to ____

28 falls between ____ and 30 and is closer to ____

69 falls between ____ and 70 and is closer to ____

53 falls between ____ and 60 and is closer to ____

(5) Joseph and Joshua were gathering eggs in the hen house. Joseph had 18 brown eggs and Joshua had 15 white eggs. Which boy gathered the most eggs?_____ How many more? ____ How many did the boys gather together? ____ _____

Terry and Ashley went rock hunting. Ashley found 32 rocks and Terry found 78 rocks. Together they found how many rocks? ____ _____ Which girl found the most rocks? _____ How many more? ____

(6) **What animal keeps the best time?**

H	D	T	G	W	A	O	C
164	52	102	44	134	101	54	113

$$64 + 37$$ ○

$$36 + 98$$ ○

$$25 + 76$$ ○

$$15 + 87$$ ○

$$74 + 39$$ ○

$$78 + 86$$ ○

$$86 - 34$$ ○

$$79 - 25$$ ○

$$54 - 10$$ ○

10

1 penny	**1 nickel**	**1 dime**	**1 quarter**	**1 half dollar**
1 cent	5 cents	10 cents	25 cents	50 cents
1 ¢	5 ¢	10 ¢	25 ¢	50 ¢
$0.01	$0.05	$0.10	$0.25	$0.50

1   Write the value of each set of coins.

_____   _____   _____

_____   _____

2   Write the numbers.

58 = ___ tens + 18 ones   81 = ___ tens + 11 ones

72 = ___ tens + 12 ones   43 = ___ tens + 13 ones

34 = ___ tens + 14 ones   16 = ___ tens + 16 ones

69 = ___ tens + 19 ones   95 = ___ tens + 15 ones

27 = ___ tens + 17 ones   60 = ___ tens + 10 ones

3 Write the correct time.

_____ _____ _____ _____ _____

When the sun goes down the time is (A.M. or P.M.)? ____
When the sun comes up the time is (A.M. or P.M.)? ____

4 Write the numbers.

83 falls between ____ and ____ and is closer to ____

46 falls between ____ and ____ and is closer to ____

13 falls between ____ and ____ and is closer to ____

98 falls between ____ and ____ and is closer to ____

52 falls between ____ and ____ and is closer to ____

5 Find the sum.

159	346	507	618	465	419	114	326
+ 826	+ 625	+ 316	+ 213	+ 308	+ 432	+ 609	+ 258

238	154	829	753	236	104	239	428
+ 257	+ 706	+ 155	+ 118	+ 739	+ 458	+ 421	+ 356

6 Write the addition facts having a sum of:

1 **Find the sum.**

¹453	addend	¹648	_____
+ 271	addend	+ 290	_____
724	sum	938	

210	345	392	380	578	635	643	193
+ 390	+ 160	+ 486	+ 342	+ 270	+ 194	+ 185	+ 774

184	236	481	421	362	290	266	347
+ 175	+ 281	+ 385	+ 196	+ 154	+ 148	+ 693	+ 571

2 **Write the value of each set in 2 ways.**

_____ _____

_____ _____

_____ _____

_____ _____

_____ _____

13

3 Write the numbers.

82 = _7_ tens + _12_ ones   75 = ___ tens + ___ ones

37 = ___ tens + ___ ones   26 = ___ tens + ___ ones

54 = ___ tens + ___ ones   13 = ___ tens + ___ ones

61 = ___ tens + ___ ones   79 = ___ tens + ___ ones

4 Write the numbers.

63 rounded to the nearest ten will be either ____ or ____. Which is correct? ____

82 rounded to the nearest ten will be either ____ or ____. Which is correct? ____

46 rounded to the nearest ten will be either ____ or ____. Which is correct? ____

58 rounded to the nearest ten will be either ____ or ____. Which is correct? ____

29 rounded to the nearest ten will be either ____ or ____. Which is correct? ____

5 Write the subtraction facts having a difference of:

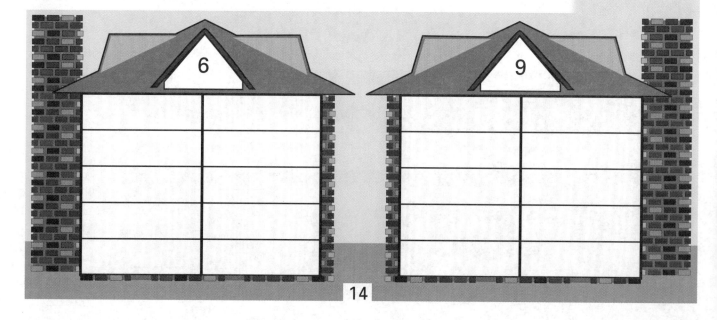

1 **Write the numbers.**

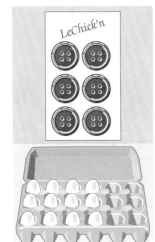

2 + 2 + 2 = _____
three 2's = _____
3 x 2 = _____

3 + 3 = _____
two 3's = _____
2 x 3 = _____

4 + 4 + 4 = _____
three 4's = _____
3 x 4 = _____

3 + 3 + 3 + 3 = _____
four 3's = _____
4 x 3 = _____

2 **Write the numbers.**

37 rounded to the nearest ten will be either _____ or _____.
Which is correct? _____

91 rounded to the nearest ten will be either _____ or _____.
Which is correct? _____

14 rounded to the nearest ten will be either _____ or _____.
Which is correct? _____

76 rounded to the nearest ten will be either _____ or _____.
Which is correct? _____

52 rounded to the nearest ten will be either _____ or _____.
Which is correct? _____

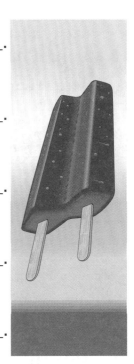

3 **Find the sum. Write the terms.**

625	_____	273	924	713	562	346
+ 733	_____	+ 812	+ 553	+ 575	+ 822	+ 851
	_____					

914	643	945	554	223	833	951	602
+ 642	+ 826	+ 742	+ 613	+ 911	+ 543	+ 432	+ 574

1 dollar	5 dollars	10 dollars	20 dollars
100 cents	500 cents	1,000 cents	2,000 cents
100¢	500¢	1,000¢	2,000¢
$1.00	$5.00	$10.00	$20.00

(4) **Write the value of each set.**

$ _____ . $ _____ . $ _____ .

$ _____ .

(5) **Find the difference.**

82	74	84	59	87	85	98	64
- 50	- 62	- 73	- 48	- 24	- 41	- 60	- 34

59	96	69	75	48	93	76	85
- 21	- 21	- 43	- 25	- 13	- 53	- 35	- 13

(6) **Write the addition facts having a sum of:**

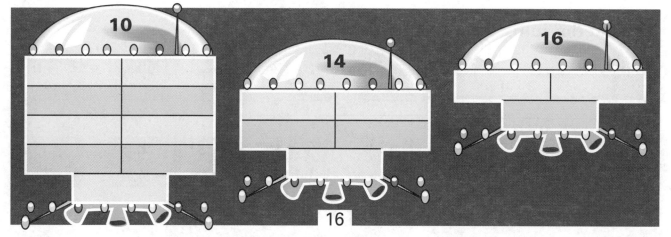

16

1 Write the value of each set.

$ _____ . _____

$ _____ . _____

$ _____ . _____

$ _____ . _____

$ _____ . _____

$ _____ . _____

2 Round the numbers to the nearest 10.

48	_____	56	_____	62	_____
71	_____	89	_____	13	_____
94	_____	27	_____	74	_____
32	_____	42	_____	38	_____

3 Find the difference.

39 - 19	84 - 53	57 - 45	27 - 23	84 - 62	15 - 12	92 - 41	67 - 30
95 - 20	83 - 82	76 - 15	89 - 47	97 - 64	69 - 60	86 - 31	87 - 77

17

4 **Write the numbers.**

5 + 5 + 5 = ____

three 5's = ____

3 x 5 = ____

3 + 3 + 3 + 3 + 3 = ____   five 3's = ____   5 x 3 = ____

2 + 2 + 2 + 2 = ____

four 2's = ____

4 x 2 = ____

4 + 4 = ____

two 4's = ____

2 x 4 = ____

5 **Find the sum.**

621 + 739	278 + 819	923 + 557	713 + 578	965 + 128	719 + 846	643 + 829	452 + 938

945 + 416	225 + 915	438 + 645	964 + 209	527 + 864	576 + 706	815 + 829	649 + 734

The numbers being added in an addition problem are called _____.
The answer in an addition problem is called the _____.

6 **Write the subtraction facts having a difference of:**

4   **1**   **8**

_____ _____   _____ _____   _____ _____

_____ _____   _____ _____   _____ _____

_____ _____   _____ _____   _____ _____

_____ _____   _____ _____   _____ _____

_____ _____   _____ _____   _____ _____

18

1 **Match the numbers.** 8 pts. total for this exercise.

four hundred eighty-six	864	six hundred forty-eight	680
eight hundred forty-six	486	six hundred eighty-four	684
eight hundred sixty-four	468	six hundred eighty	604
four hundred sixty-eight	846	six hundred four	648

2 **Write the correct letter beside the ordinal number.** 12 pts.

E   N   C   Y   C   L   O   P   E   D   I   A

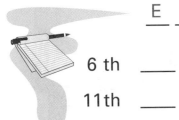

6 th ____   10th ____   7 th ____   3 rd ____

11th ____   2 nd ____   1 st ____   12th ____

5 th ____   8 th ____   4 th ____   9 th ____

3 **Write the numbers.** 18 pts. total for this exercise.

6,783 = _____ thousands + ____ hundreds + __ tens + __ ones

2,594 = _____ thousands + ____ hundreds + __ tens + __ ones

5 thousands + 8 hundreds + 0 tens + 4 ones =

_____ + ____ + __ + __ = _____

9 thousands + 2 hundreds + 6 tens + 2 ones =

_____ + ____ + __ + __ = _____

4 **Find the sum.** 8 pts. total for this exercise.

59	37	82	65	94	47	58	62
+ 37	+ 54	+ 57	+ 79	+ 44	+ 15	+ 68	+ 54

5 Round the numbers to the nearest 10. 8 pts. total for this exercise.

38 ____   61 ____   29 ____   84 ____

42 ____   76 ____   57 ____   13 ____

6 Write the correct time. 4 pts. total for this exercise.

_____   _____   _____   _____

7 Write the value of the blue digit. 4 pts. total for this exercise.

4,872 _____   7,109 _____

3,956 _____   5,284 _____

8 Find the difference. 8 pts. total for this exercise.

89	76	87	96	57	69	58	42
- 88	- 53	- 57	- 65	- 42	- 13	- 32	- 21

70 Total pts.

1 Write "even" if the number of letters in the words is even. Write "odd" if the number of letters in the words is odd.

addend _____	product _____	dimes _____
sum _____	multiplication _____	subtraction _____
difference _____	quarters _____	hour _____

2 Write the value of each set.

$ _____ .

$ _____ .

$ _____ .

$ _____ .

$ _____ .

$ _____ .

3 Find the sum.

127 + 689	256 + 276	254 + 597	373 + 368	567 + 243	546 + 196	457 + 367	353 + 168

275 + 498	367 + 245	389 + 123	469 + 282	698 + 193	487 + 443	689 + 275	474 + 289

Find the difference. Round the answers in the last row to the nearest 10.

79 - 19	68 - 10	49 - 23	24 - 10	93 - 73	18 - 14	57 - 43	69 - 35

48 - 35	56 - 24	97 - 64	88 - 71	96 - 42	69 - 28	85 - 21	87 - 45

_____   _____   _____   _____   _____   _____   _____   _____

5 Write the missing equation for the multiplication fact pair.

6 x 3 = 18 3 x 6 = 18	7 x 5 = 35	4 x 9 = 36	5 x 2 = 10
8 x 1 = 8	2 x 7 = 14	9 x 8 = 72	3 x 5 = 15
4 x 6 = 24	1 x 3 = 3	6 x 8 = 48	8 x 4 = 32

6 Find the answers.

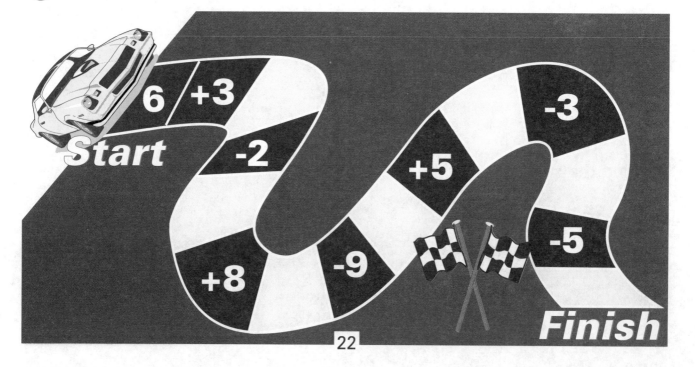

6 +3   -2   +8   -9   +5   -3   -5

Start   Finish

22

① **Write the largest number possible.**

1 8 6 4 3   2 0 7 9 5   6 1 4 9 3   2 8 5 7 0

_____   _____   _____   _____

② **Write < or >.**

63 ____ 36	
85 ____ 91	
94 ____ 48	

26 ____ 84	
71 ____ 55	
18 ____ 13	

57 ____ 72	
49 ____ 69	
32 ____ 27	

③ **Write the value of each set.**

$ _____ . _____ $ _____ . _____ $ _____ . _____

④ **Circle the correct answer.**

There is an (even or odd) number of vowels in the alphabet.

There is an (even or odd) number of donuts in a dozen.

There is an (even or odd) number of days in a week.

There is an (even or odd) number of months in a year.

There is an (even or odd) number of inches in a foot.

⑤ Match the figure with its name.

sphere   circle

triangle   cylinder

diamond   pentagon

pyramid   cone

rectangle   cube

octagon   hexagon

square   oval

⑥ Multiply the numbers.

10	0	10	1	0	10	1	1	10
x 9	x 7	x 1	x 3	x 1	x 0	x 5	x 0	x 7

1	0	10	1	1	10	0	10	0
x 4	x 4	x 6	x 6	x 9	x 3	x 5	x 5	x 9

0	1	10	0	1	10	1	1	10
x 8	x 8	x 4	x 6	x 2	x 8	x 7	x 1	x 2

⑦ Find the sum.

724	216	435	374	855	793	589	386
+ 436	+ 745	+ 843	+ 981	+ 354	+ 177	+ 703	+ 941

24

1 Write the missing fact needed to form pairs and multiply.

1 x 7		10 x 3		10 x 7		1 x 3	

10 x 4		10 x 8		1 x 2		0 x 4	

0 x 9		1 x 6		10 x 5		1 x 9	

2 Write the largest number possible.

3 6 1 7 5   2 9 4 8 0   8 3 5 7 4   6 0 9 1 2

_____   _____   _____   _____

3 Match large to small.

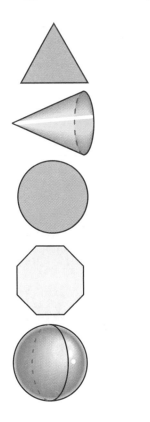
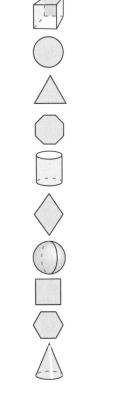
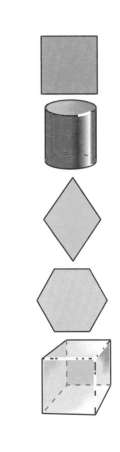

25

4 Write < or >.

136 ____ 257	407 ____ 704	782 ____ 287
827 ____ 938	325 ____ 253	915 ____ 519
549 ____ 594	618 ____ 186	276 ____ 167

5 Write the value of each set.

$ _____ . _____ $ _____ . _____ $ _____ . _____

$ _____ . _____ $ _____ . _____ $ _____ . _____

6 Find the sum.

| I = 1 | IV = 4 | V = 5 | IX = 9 | X = 10 | XL = 40 | L = 50 |

1 Write the Roman numerals.

12 _____	5 _____	9 _____	3 _____
6 _____	13 _____	17 _____	16 _____
19 _____	2 _____	1 _____	8 _____
4 _____	11 _____	15 _____	18 _____
14 _____	20 _____	7 _____	10 _____

2 Find the difference. Write the terms.

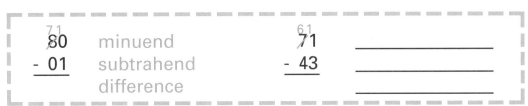

71	61
8̶0̶ minuend	7̶1̶ _____
- 01 subtrahend	- 43 _____
difference	_____

| 90 | 43 | 52 | 30 | 86 | 81 | 28 | 45 |
| - 14 | - 15 | - 33 | - 18 | - 37 | - 65 | - 9 | - 28 |

| 63 | 82 | 34 | 71 | 75 | 12 | 56 | 64 |
| - 57 | - 56 | - 26 | - 68 | - 27 | - 9 | - 47 | - 16 |

3 Write the largest number possible.

| 3 1 5 8 4 | 2 9 6 0 7 | 8 2 1 4 9 | 6 0 3 7 5 |
| _____ | _____ | _____ | _____ |

| 2 3 8 6 4 | 5 9 0 7 1 | 8 6 5 4 1 | 3 5 7 2 4 |
| _____ | _____ | _____ | _____ |

(4) **Write < or >.**

8,384 ___ 4,184	1,704 ___ 1,407	3,591 ___ 5,913
3,596 ___ 5,963	6,238 ___ 2,638	7,073 ___ 3,707
2,720 ___ 7,220	5,942 ___ 9,452	4,162 ___ 1,624

(5) **Multiply the numbers.**

6	0	5	1	7	10	0	8	1
x 5	x 7	x 1	x 3	x 5	x 4	x 2	x 5	x 6

10	10	5	0	5	1	10	5	9
x 5	x 8	x 5	x 4	x 4	x 9	x 3	x 3	x 0

5	9	0	10	1	10	4	6	10
x 2	x 5	x 3	x 6	x 7	x 2	x 1	x 0	x 7

(6) **Match the halves.**

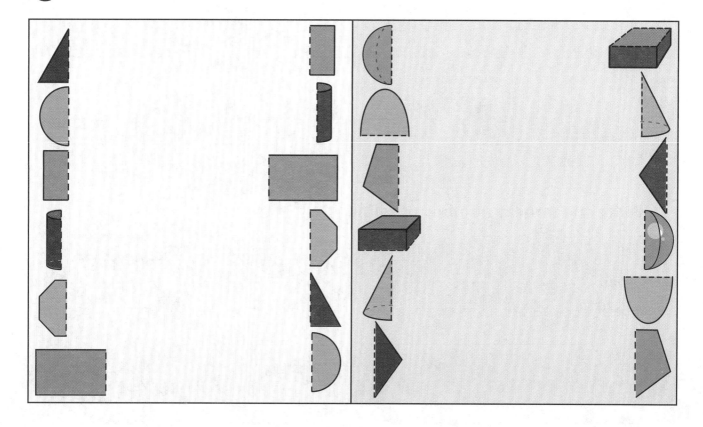

1 **Write the fractional part that is shaded.**

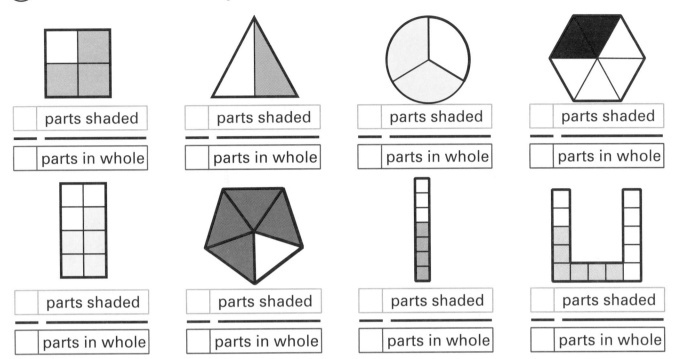

	parts shaded
	parts in whole

	parts shaded
	parts in whole

	parts shaded
	parts in whole

	parts shaded
	parts in whole

	parts shaded
	parts in whole

	parts shaded
	parts in whole

	parts shaded
	parts in whole

	parts shaded
	parts in whole

The top number is called the _____ .

The bottom number is called the _____ .

2 **Write the Roman numerals.**

I = 1	V = 5	X = 10	L = 50	C = 100	D = 500	M = 1000

2 _____   16 _____   11 _____   3 _____

10 _____   8 _____   14 _____   13 _____

15 _____   12 _____   1 _____   7 _____

19 _____   4 _____   18 _____   17 _____

5 _____   20 _____   6 _____   9 _____

3 **Multiply the numbers.**

6 x 5	1 x 5	10 x 5	5 x 2	10 x 3	8 x 5	0 x 7	5 x 0	2 x 1

5	0	10	5	1	9	1	7	5
x 3	x 4	x 9	x 1	x 8	x 5	x 0	x 5	x 4

4 Find the difference. Write the terms.

90		72	83	81	54	47
- 74	_____	- 34	- 47	- 78	- 18	- 38

_____

82	56	90	74	93	65	31	61
- 17	- 47	- 17	- 65	- 44	- 27	- 25	- 52

5 Write the names.

_____   _____   _____

_____   _____   _____

_____   _____   _____

_____   _____   _____

_____   _____

6 Jessica and Suzette helped their mother fold the laundry. Jessica folded 28 boy socks and Suzette folded 56 girl socks. How many socks did they fold together? _____ _____ Who folded the most socks? _____ How many more? _____

30

1 Add 10 to each number.

34 _____   136 _____   79 _____   315 _____

90 _____   8 _____   726 _____   42 _____

861 _____   53 _____   471 _____   87 _____

2 Write the Arabic numbers.

X _____   VI _____   XV _____

IV _____   XIV _____   V _____

XVII _____   III _____   IX _____

VII _____   XII _____   XX _____

3 Multiply and write the missing fact to form pairs.

Fact		Fact
5 x 2	10	2 x 5
5 x 9		
5 x 1		
5 x 8		
4 x 5		
7 x 5		
3 x 5		
6 x 5		

Fact		Fact
3 x 10		
1 x 8		
4 x 0		
7 x 0		
10 x 6		
7 x 1		
0 x 1		
1 x 2		

4 Beth was 6 years older than Anna. If Anna is 5, how old is Beth? _____
_____ If Beth is 15, how old is Anna? _____ _____

31

Julia and David are 9 years apart in age. If Julia is the oldest and 15 years old, how old is David? _____ _____ When David is 10 years old, how old will Julia be? _____ _____

5 **Write the fractional part that is *not* shaded.**

| ___ | parts not shaded | ___ | parts not shaded | ___ | parts not shaded | ___ | parts not shaded |
| ___ | parts in whole | ___ | parts in whole | ___ | parts in whole | ___ | parts in whole |

| ___ | parts not shaded | ___ | parts not shaded | ___ | parts not shaded | ___ | parts not shaded |
| ___ | parts in whole | ___ | parts in whole | ___ | parts in whole | ___ | parts in whole |

The number of parts used is called the _____ .

The number of parts into which the whole is divided is called the

_____ .

6 **Write the numbers.**

three hundred eighty-six	_____	eight hundred forty-three	_____
four hundred ninety-two	_____	two hundred sixty-four	_____
five hundred thirty-seven	_____	seven hundred nine	_____
one hundred fifty	_____	nine hundred seventy-five	_____

7 **Find the difference.**

| $6.92 | $9.81 | $8.73 | $8.41 | $3.70 | $9.63 | $6.95 | $3.74 |
| - 4.85 | - 5.63 | - 6.45 | - 3.26 | - 1.51 | - 3.18 | - 3.68 | - 2.39 |

32

① **Write the numbers in expanded form.**

3,000 + 200 + 60 + 5 = (___ x 1,000) + (___ x 100) + (___ x 10) + (___ x 1)

6,000 + 800 + 40 + 7 = (___ x 1,000) + (___ x 100) + (___ x 10) + (___ x 1)

9,000 + 100 + 30 + 2 = (___ x 1,000) + (___ x 100) + (___ x 10) + (___ x 1)

4,000 + 700 + 90 + 8 = (___ x 1,000) + (___ x 100) + (___ x 10) + (___ x 1)

5,000 + 400 + 50 + 0 = (___ x 1,000) + (___ x 100) + (___ x 10) + (___ x 1)

② **Shade the shape for each fractional part.**

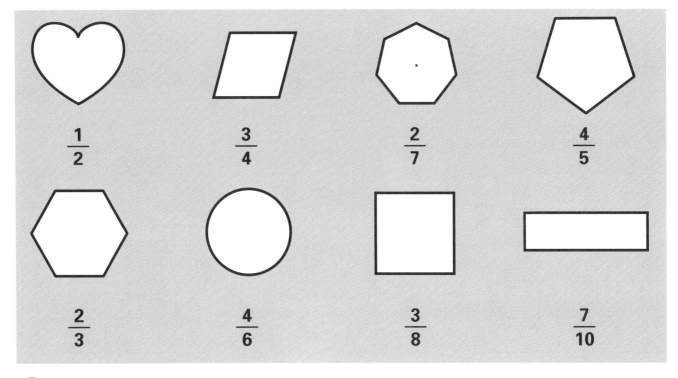

③ **Find the sum.**

$ 28.47 + 60.86	$ 72.61 + 14.59	$ 62.54 + 32.96	$ 62.58 + 10.52	$ 41.53 + 52.78	$ 51.96 + 37.17	$ 31.25 + 20.97
$ 45.98 + 12.78	$ 31.79 + 65.49	$ 40.69 + 26.95	$ 41.82 + 30.69	$ 63.97 + 4.38	$ 30.85 + 24.48	$ 42.46 + 56.89

④ Write the word numbers.

345 _____   583 _____

830 _____   724 _____

261 _____   698 _____

107 _____   476 _____

⑤ Write the Arabic numbers.

XVIII _____   X _____   XIII _____

V _____   VIII _____   XV _____

XI _____   IX _____   II _____

XII _____   XVI _____   IV _____

⑥ Multiply the numbers.

X	5	1	0	10
1				
3				
8				
5				

X	10	5	0	1
2				
7				
4				
6				

X	1	5	10	0
3				
9				
8				
0				

⑦ John weighs 38 pounds. Jerry weighs 46 pounds. Tom weighs 41 pounds. How much do John and Jerry weigh together? _____ _____ How much do Tom and Jerry weigh together? _____ _____ How much do Tom and John weigh together? _____ _____ Who is the heaviest? _____ Who weighs the least? _____ How much do the three boys weigh together? _____ _____

34

1 **Write the correct time.**

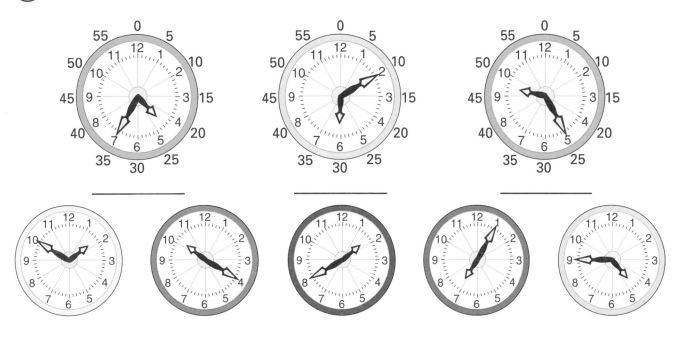

_____   _____   _____

_____   _____   _____   _____   _____

When supper is ready, the time is (A.M. or P.M.)? _____
When it is afternoon, the time is (A.M. or P.M.)? _____

2 **Find the sum.**

2,679	1,637	3,917	3,915	1,845	3,208	5,429
+ 3,408	+ 4,619	+ 663	+ 3,476	+ 3,448	+ 5,853	+ 3,741

2,468	2,709	1,803	2,954	1,348	3,657	2,713
+ 1,729	+ 5,539	+ 4,729	+ 6,219	+ 1,705	+ 4,807	+ 968

3 **Match the word to its symbol.**

add	x	greater than	¢
subtract	+	less than	>
multiply	=	dollars	<
equal	-	cents	$

④ Write the numbers in expanded form.

2,000 + 300 + 70 + 6 = (2 x _____) + (3 x _____) + (7 x _____) + (6 x _____)

7,000 + 900 + 10 + 3 = (7 x _____) + (9 x _____) + (1 x _____) + (3 x _____)

1,000 + 500 + 40 + 1 = (1 x _____) + (5 x _____) + (4 x _____) + (1 x _____)

8,000 + 100 + 20 + 4 = (8 x _____) + (1 x _____) + (2 x _____) + (4 x _____)

4,000 + 600 + 80 + 9 = (4 x _____) + (6 x _____) + (8 x _____) + (9 x _____)

⑤ Shade the rectangles for each fractional part.

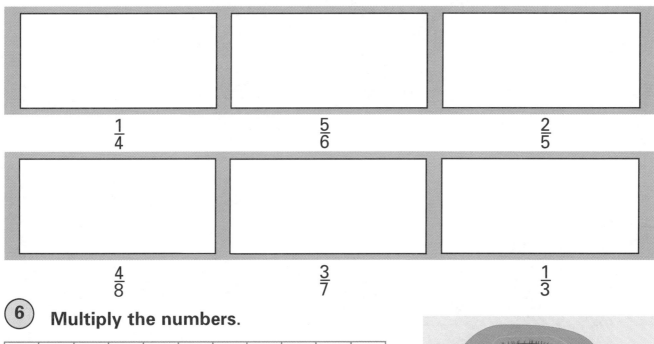

$\frac{1}{4}$ $\frac{5}{6}$ $\frac{2}{5}$

$\frac{4}{8}$ $\frac{3}{7}$ $\frac{1}{3}$

⑥ Multiply the numbers.

X	10	4	7	2	9	1	6	5	3	8
5										

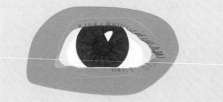

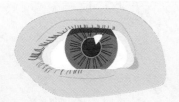

X	6	8	1	10	4	7	2	9	5	3
2										

⑦ Sally, Mary, and Sue have black eyes. Paul and James have brown eyes. How many brown eyes are there? _____ How many black eyes are there? _____ How many eyes do all five children have? _____ Did you add or multiply to get the last answer? _____

36

1 Write the smallest number possible.

2 7 3 8 5		4 1 9 6 0		9 3 1 7 2		5 8 4 0 6	

_____   _____   _____   _____

2 Multiply the numbers.

X	10	100	1,000
26			
34			
58			
93			
72			
47			

X	10	100	1,000
8			
6			
3			
9			
4			
7			

X	10	100	1,000
346			
285			
974			
810			
726			
457			

3 Write the missing digit and check.

$$
\begin{array}{r} 3{,}69\square \\ +1{,}\square97 \\ \hline 5{,}289 \end{array}
\quad
\begin{array}{r} 3{,}\square4\square \\ +3{,}861 \\ \hline 7{,}708 \end{array}
\quad
\begin{array}{r} 6{,}\square56 \\ +2{,}79\square \\ \hline 9{,}746 \end{array}
\quad
\begin{array}{r} \square{,}595 \\ +1{,}5\square4 \\ \hline 6{,}149 \end{array}
\quad
\begin{array}{r} \square{,}5\square3 \\ +3{,}735 \\ \hline 9{,}328 \end{array}
\quad
\begin{array}{r} 4{,}495 \\ +3{,}\square1\square \\ \hline 8{,}306 \end{array}
\quad
\begin{array}{r} 4{,}7\square1 \\ +\square{,}697 \\ \hline 8{,}448 \end{array}
$$

$$
\begin{array}{r} 1{,}83\square \\ +1{,}\square84 \\ \hline 3{,}516 \end{array}
\quad
\begin{array}{r} \square{,}8\square0 \\ +\ \ \ 494 \\ \hline 9{,}314 \end{array}
\quad
\begin{array}{r} 1{,}18\square \\ +3{,}\square22 \\ \hline 5{,}109 \end{array}
\quad
\begin{array}{r} 2{,}6\square1 \\ +\square{,}795 \\ \hline 5{,}466 \end{array}
\quad
\begin{array}{r} \square{,}762 \\ +7{,}7\square0 \\ \hline 9{,}552 \end{array}
\quad
\begin{array}{r} 5{,}372 \\ +2{,}\square4\square \\ \hline 8{,}313 \end{array}
\quad
\begin{array}{r} 5{,}86\square \\ +2{,}\square81 \\ \hline 8{,}745 \end{array}
$$

4 Write the numbers in expanded and standard form.

$(3 \times 1{,}000) + (2 \times 100) + (6 \times 10) + (9 \times 1) =$ _____ + _____ + ____ + ____ = _____

$(6 \times 1{,}000) + (4 \times 100) + (7 \times 10) + (8 \times 1) =$ _____ + _____ + ____ + ____ = _____

$(2 \times 1{,}000) + (7 \times 100) + (8 \times 10) + (5 \times 1) =$ _____ + _____ + ____ + ____ = _____

$(7 \times 1{,}000) + (1 \times 100) + (0 \times 10) + (4 \times 1) =$ _____ + _____ + ____ + ____ = _____

⑤ Solve the equations.

n + 6̶ = 13
  - 6̶   - 6
―――――
   n = 7
check
7 + 6 = 13
	n + 5̶ = 11
	  - 5̶ - 5
	―――――
	   n = ___
	check
	___ + 5 = 11
		n + 9̶ = 17
		  - 9̶ - 9
		―――――
		   n = ___
		check
		___ + 9 = ___

n + 3 = 8
  -     -
――――
    =
check
___ + ___ = ___
	n + 7 = 13
	  - -
	――――
	    =
	check
	___ + ___ = ___
		n + 5 = 14
		  - -
		――――
		    =
		check
		___ + ___ = ___
			n + 7 = 14
			  - -
			――――
			    =
			check
			___ + ___ = ___

⑥ Write the correct time.

――――― ――――― ――――― ――――― ―――――

――――― ――――― ――――― ――――― ―――――

What is one hour later than 5:00 P.M.? _____
What is one hour earlier than 10:00 A.M.? _____

⑦ Write the correct symbol.

greater than   ____   addition   ____

dollar sign   ____   cent sign   ____

multiplication   ____   less than   ____

subtraction   ____   equal   ____

1 Write = or ≠.

6 x 10 ____ 60	8 x 100 ____ 800	218 x 1,000 ____ 21,800
35 x 100 ____ 3,500	48 x 10 ____ 4,800	10 x 100 ____ 100
86 x 1,000 ____ 8,600	516 x 10 ____ 5,160	72 x 10 ____ 7,200
732 x 100 ____ 73,200	3 x 1,000 ____ 3,000	403 x 100 ____ 4,030

2 Find the difference.

835	958	729	681	613	832	407	647
- 764	- 691	- 363	- 591	- 242	- 492	- 295	- 373

927	209	753	815	945	668	629	508
- 596	- 169	- 261	- 670	- 271	- 493	- 138	- 262

3 Write the correct time.

What time is it 2 hours before 8:00 A.M.? _____

What time is it 3 hours after 11:00 A.M.? _____

4 **Write the numbers in expanded and standard form.**

$(3 \times 1{,}000) + (1 \times 100) + (0 \times 10) + (4 \times 1) =$ _____ + _____ + ____ + ____ = _____

$(2 \times 1{,}000) + (4 \times 100) + (9 \times 10) + (8 \times 1) =$ _____ + _____ + ____ + ____ = _____

$(6 \times 1{,}000) + (7 \times 100) + (2 \times 10) + (5 \times 1) =$ _____ + _____ + ____ + ____ = _____

$(8 \times 1{,}000) + (5 \times 100) + (3 \times 10) + (4 \times 1) =$ _____ + _____ + ____ + ____ = _____

5 **Solve the equations.**

$n + 5 = 12$ $\quad - 5 \quad - 5$ $\quad\quad n = 7$ check $7 + 5 = 12$	$n + 3 = 10$	$n + 8 = 13$	$n + 4 = 9$
$n + 7 = 11$	$n + 9 = 14$	$n + 6 = 15$	$n + 1 = 8$

6 **Write the smallest number possible.**

4 7 3 8 1   5 2 6 0 9   2 4 6 1 9   8 3 0 7 5

_____   _____   _____   _____

7 **Write the missing numbers for the addition puzzle.**

1		3	8
5	8	2	
6		7	
	21		

	3	1	8
	7		14
8			14
14		12	

6		8	16
7	4		
		3	13
14		16	

① Write the value of each. 9 pts. total for this exercise.

 _____    _____    _____

 _____   _____   (one dollar bill) _____

(dime) _____    _____   (five dollar bill) _____

② Write < or >. 12 pts. total for this exercise.

38 ___ 83	43 ___ 34	49 ___ 92	91 ___ 100
114 ___ 141	107 ___ 71	82 ___ 28	777 ___ 787
308 ___ 830	392 ___ 329	561 ___ 516	111 ___ 88

③ Write the Roman numerals. 6 pts. total for this exercise.

58 _____   63 _____   24 _____

16 _____   9 _____   70 _____

④ Find the sum. 8 pts. total for this exercise.

839	560	384	953	274	414	673	781
+ 128	+ 817	+ 674	+ 644	+ 562	+ 569	+ 296	+ 175

5. Write the fractional part shaded. 4 pts. total for this exercise.

_____   _____   _____   _____

6. Multiply the numbers. 33 pts. total for this exercise.

X	3	6	7	4	9	2	8	1	10	5	0
0											
5											
1											

7. Write even or odd. 4 pts. total for this exercise.

36 _____   475 _____   389 _____   12 _____

8. Jack ran 352 yards on Tuesday and 286 on Thursday. Which day did he run the most yards? _____ How many yards did he run in the 2 days? _____ _____ 3 pts. total for this exercise.

42

1 Add 10 to each number.

236 _____	97 _____	490 _____	12 _____
15 _____	538 _____	174 _____	689 _____
7,263 _____	8 _____	1,340 _____	23 _____
51 _____	849 _____	2,156 _____	78 _____

2 Solve the equations and check.

$n + 3 = 12$ $- 3 \quad - 3$ _____ check	$n + 8 = 15$	$n + 4 = 10$	$n + 5 = 9$

$n + 7 = 13$	$n + 9 = 15$	$n + 6 = 11$	$n + 1 = 6$

3 Multiply the numbers.

X	1	2	3	4	5	6	7	8	9	0
3										

X	3	0	5	8	4	1	7	2	6	9
2										

4 Write the smallest number possible.

7 1 0 8 3	2 5 4 9 6	3 9 8 6 0	4 7 1 5 2
_____	_____	_____	_____

Write = or ≠.

 _____ 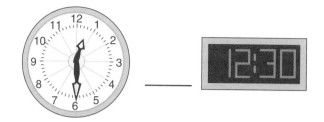 _____

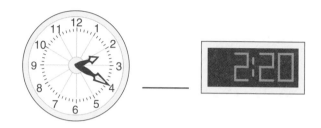 _____ 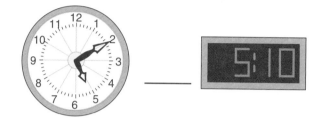 _____

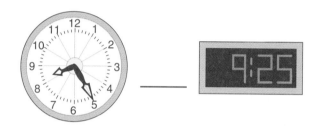 _____ 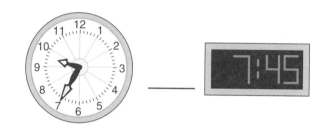 _____

6 **Find the difference.**

706	878	947	929	569	708	649	826
- 126	- 295	- 163	- 475	- 287	- 632	- 190	- 374

314	439	815	602	529	654	734	555
- 183	- 182	- 643	- 482	- 348	- 83	- 351	- 192

7 Sam received 4 A's, 2 B's, and 1 C. Mike received 2 A's, 5 B's, and 0 C's. Who received the most A's? _____ Who received the most B's? _____ Who received the most C's? _____ How many A's did they receive in all? _____ _____ How many B's did they receive in all? _____ _____ How many grades did they each get? _____ _____

1 Write the numbers.

(4 + 8) + 3 = _____ + 3 = _____

4 + (8 + 3) = 4 + _____ = _____

(2 + 6) + 4 = _____ + 4 = _____

2 + (6 + 4) = 2 + _____ = _____

(3 + 9) + 5 = _____ + 5 = _____

3 + (9 + 5) = 3 + _____ = _____

4 + (9 + 3) = 4 + _____ = _____

(4 + 9) + 3 = _____ + 3 = _____

2 Write the numbers.

152 falls between 150 and _____.

278 falls between 270 and _____.

516 falls between 510 and _____.

834 falls between 830 and _____.

623 falls between 620 and _____.

361 falls between 360 and _____.

789 falls between 780 and _____.

947 falls between 940 and _____.

3 Write < or >.

61 ___ 37	
47 ___ 95	
83 ___ 72	

151 ___ 128	
260 ___ 239	
719 ___ 791	

266 ___ 411	
529 ___ 347	
694 ___ 273	

4 Find the sum. Check the answers.

23	17	28	25	26	18	24	21
19	45	23	19	16	25	35	38
+ 24	+ 17	+ 36	+ 32	+ 52	+ 43	+ 36	+ 19

(5) Write the terms.

4	multiplicand
x 5	multiplier
20	product

7	_____
x 2	_____
	_____

Find the product.

10	3	9	5	2	8	5	3	5
x 3	x 3	x 2	x 3	x 8	x 3	x 8	x 0	x 2

3	7	9	5	3	9	7	2	3
x 4	x 5	x 3	x 6	x 1	x 5	x 3	x 6	x 2

(6) Solve the equations and check.

n + 2 = 9	n + 3 = 11	n + 8 = 16	n + 5 = 10
n + 4 = 12	n + 7 = 13	n + 6 = 14	n + 9 = 15

(7) Write 2 addition and 2 subtraction facts.

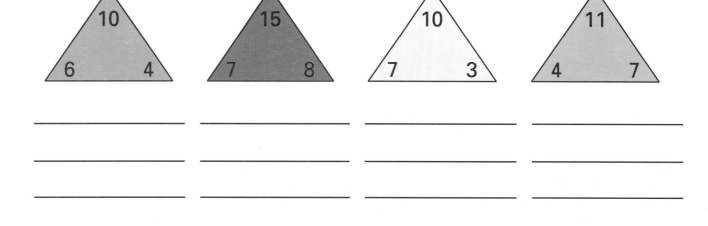

46

(1) **Write the numbers.**

373 falls between _____ and 380 and is closer to _____.

418 falls between _____ and 420 and is closer to _____.

854 falls between _____ and 860 and is closer to _____.

531 falls between _____ and 540 and is closer to _____.

946 falls between _____ and 950 and is closer to _____.

607 falls between _____ and 610 and is closer to _____.

729 falls between _____ and 730 and is closer to _____.

263 falls between _____ and 270 and is closer to _____.

(2) **Find the sum. Write odd or even below each answer.**

73	21	86	30	93	14	31	62
76	92	51	74	21	82	95	42
+ 10	+ 85	+ 22	+ 45	+ 44	+ 82	+ 52	+ 72

_____ _____ _____ _____ _____ _____ _____ _____

The numbers being added are called the _____. The answer in an addition problem is called the _____.

(3) **Find the product. Write the terms.**

5	_____
x 3	_____
	_____

7	8	1	10	3	8	3	4	9
x 2	x 3	x 3	x 3	x 5	x 2	x 9	x 3	x 2

3	2	3	6	3	10	2	2	3
x 8	x 5	x 3	x 2	x 6	x 2	x 3	x 4	x 7

4 Write < or >.

258 ___ 372	625 ___ 934	761 ___ 617
840 ___ 496	183 ___ 517	304 ___ 340
372 ___ 327	593 ___ 604	810 ___ 601

5 Write the numbers.

$(2 + 9) + 5 =$ ___ $+ 5 =$ ___

$2 + (9 + 5) = 2 +$ ___ $=$ ___

$(1 + 3) + 7 =$ ___ $+$ ___ $=$ ___

$1 + (3 + 7) =$ ___ $+$ ___ $=$ ___

$(4 + 5) + 6 =$ ___ $+$ ___ $=$ ___

$4 + (5 + 6) =$ ___ $+$ ___ $=$ ___

$9 + (4 + 3) =$ ___ $+$ ___ $=$ ___

$(9 + 4) + 3 =$ ___ $+$ ___ $=$ ___

6 Solve the equations and check.

$n + 8 = 17$	$n + 9 = 16$	$n + 6 = 13$	$n + 7 = 12$
$n + 4 = 12$	$n + 3 = 12$	$n + 4 = 11$	$n + 8 = 11$

7 Alice had 3 quarters, 2 dimes, a nickel, and 3 pennies in her purse. Sarah had 2 quarters, 4 dimes, and 3 nickels in her purse. How much money did Alice have? ___ How much money did Sarah have? ___ How much money did the girls have altogether? ___ Did Alice have more or less than a dollar? ___ Did Sarah have more or less than Alice? ___ By how much? ___

48

1 **Circle coins needed to equal $1.00.**

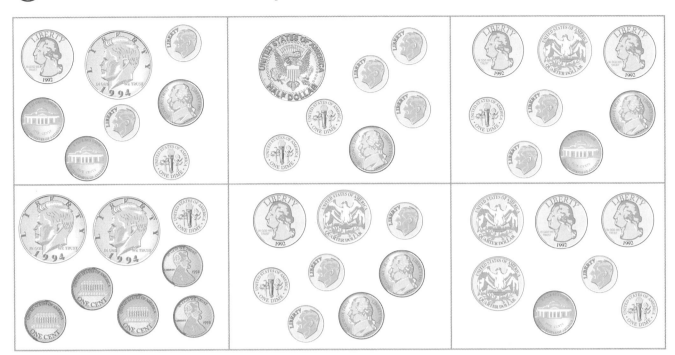

2 **Write the numbers.**

$(1 + 4) + 5 = 1 + (4 + 5)$
_____ $+ 5 =$ 1+ _____
_____ $=$ _____

$6 + (8 + 0) = (6 + 8) + 0$
$6 +$ _____ $=$ _____ $+ 0$
_____ $=$ _____

$(3 + 9) + 2 = 3 + (9 + 2)$
_____ $+ 2 =$ 3+ _____
_____ $=$ _____

$7 + (4 + 1) = (7 + 4) + 1$
$7 +$ _____ $=$ _____ $+ 1$
_____ $=$ _____

3 **Find the product.**

9	2	3	5	2	3	8	4	2
x 3	x 7	x 5	x 7	x 9	x 7	x 2	x 3	x 5

10	3	5	8	1	5	3	6	0
x 3	x 3	x 5	x 5	x 3	x 9	x 6	x 2	x 3

The answer to a multiplication problem is called the _____.

49

4 **Write < or >.**

2,348 ____ 6,753   4,123 ____ 4,356   2,891 ____ 2,819

4,195 ____ 8,437   6,571 ____ 6,284   5,626 ____ 5,662

5,873 ____ 3,684   9,837 ____ 9,495   8,437 ____ 8,473

9,019 ____ 7,926   3,648 ____ 3,912   7,241 ____ 7,214

5 **Write the numbers.**

483 falls between _____ and _____ and is closer to _____.

296 falls between _____ and _____ and is closer to _____.

731 falls between _____ and _____ and is closer to _____.

579 falls between _____ and _____ and is closer to _____.

147 falls between _____ and _____ and is closer to _____.

824 falls between _____ and _____ and is closer to _____.

6 **Find the sum. Write odd or even below each answer.**

13	61	82	34	18	70	21	72
95	68	65	27	44	38	98	38
+ 46	+ 27	+ 15	+ 84	+ 62	+ 39	+ 43	+ 45

____ ____ ____ ____ ____ ____ ____ ____

93	46	40	37	19	25	51	62
46	98	89	65	58	78	99	37
+ 27	+ 31	+ 27	+ 54	+ 70	+ 63	+ 49	+ 48

____ ____ ____ ____ ____ ____ ____ ____

7 **Write one addition and one subtraction word problem using money. Find the answers.**

50

1 **Write the numbers.**

483 is closest to _____.   256 is closest to _____.

197 is closest to _____.   522 is closest to _____.

809 is closest to _____.   634 is closest to _____.

2 **Circle the coins needed to equal 80¢.**

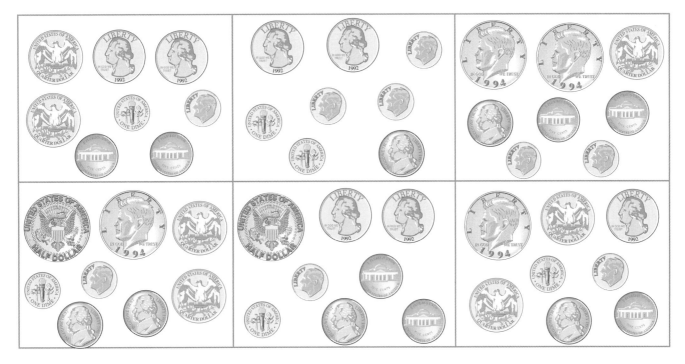

3 **Match the word to its symbol.**

add	x	greater than	¢
subtract	+	less than	>
multiply	=	dollars	<
equal	-	cents	$

4 **Find the difference.**

536	528	954	829	783	739	769	975
- 246	- 195	- 772	- 739	- 190	- 291	- 194	- 283

51

913	865	839	647	828	616	427	933
- 472	- 494	- 166	- 385	- 368	- 532	- 355	- 681

⑤ **Solve the equations and check.**

n + 3 = 11	n + 5 = 12	n + 7 = 13	n + 8 = 14
n + 9 = 15	n + 2 = 10	n + 4 = 9	n + 6 = 12

⑥ **Write the numbers.**

(3 + 7) + 5 = 3 + (7 + 5)
____ + 5 = 3 + ____
____ = ____

1 + (8 + 6) = (1 + 8) + 6
____ + ____ = ____ + ____
____ = ____

2 + (9 + 4) = (2 + 9) + 4
____ + ____ = ____ + ____
____ = ____

7 + (2 + 6) = (7 + 2) + 6
____ + ____ = ____ + ____
____ = ____

⑦ **Find the product.**

X	2	5	3
6			
8			
7			

X	4	9	0
1			
3			
5			

X	10	100	1,000
8			
24			
156			

1 **Match the figure to its name.**

 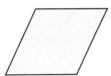 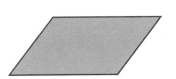 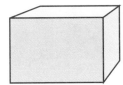

trapezoid   rhombus   parallelogram   rectangular prism

   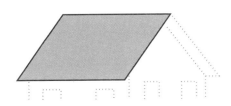

2 **Round the numbers to the nearest 10.**

368 _____	843 _____	439 _____	906 _____
627 _____	477 _____	878 _____	172 _____
259 _____	514 _____	751 _____	563 _____

3 **Find the difference.**

933	719	952	357	806	528	847	615
- 373	- 527	- 490	- 262	- 236	- 180	- 581	- 230

429	945	208	612	815	762	954	806
- 356	- 170	- 164	- 351	- 764	- 372	- 473	- 372

4 **Write the correct symbols.**

equal _____   subtract _____

add _____   less than _____

cents _____   greater than _____

multiply _____   dollars _____

(5) Circle the amount needed to equal:

$ 1.78

$ 1.46

$ 1.18

(6) Find the product.

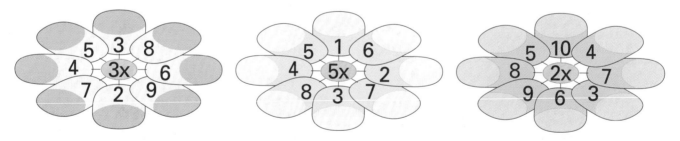

First flower: 3x with petals 5, 3, 8, 4, 6, 7, 2, 9

Second flower: 5x with petals 5, 1, 6, 4, 2, 8, 3, 7

Third flower: 2x with petals 5, 10, 4, 8, 7, 9, 6, 3

(7) At his vegetable stand, Jack sold 6 watermelons each day for 10 days. How many watermelons did he sell in all?

At the fruit stand, apples were 8¢ each, oranges were 5¢ each, bananas were 7¢ each, and grapefruit were 6¢ each. What would 10 apples cost? _____ What would 100 grapefruit cost? _____ What would 100 bananas cost? _____ What would 1,000 oranges cost?

_____

54

1 Circle the object that is a different shape.

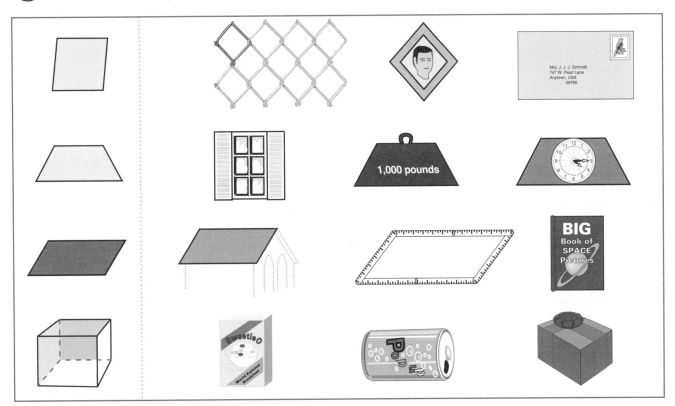

2 Write = or ≠.

V ___ 5	X ___ 5	VI ___ 6	VIII ___ 8
XII ___ 7	XIX ___ 9	XIV ___ 16	XIII ___ 13
XVII ___ 17	IV ___ 4	II ___ 2	IX ___ 11

3 Find the sum and check. Write the terms.

```
  306        _____
  476        _____
+ 114        _____
             _____
```

154	246	343	516
214	238	218	145
+ 229	+ 315	+ 127	+ 234

439	314	121	127	113	514	248	217
201	258	166	318	429	163	105	273
+ 225	+ 412	+ 509	+ 432	+ 243	+ 217	+ 315	+ 306

55

4 Write +, -, or x.

product _____   difference _____

left _____   more than _____

altogether _____ in all _____

sum _____   both _____

less _____   and _____

5 Find the product.

1 x 6	6 x 3	5 x 6	6 x 9	6 x 5	3 x 6	6 x 7	8 x 6	6 x 2

6 x 4	7 x 6	2 x 6	6 x 6	9 x 6	6 x 8	6 x 1	4 x 6

6

(crossword grid with numbered cells 1–13)

Across

1.
```
  36
+ 98
```

4.
```
  5
x 9
```

6.
```
  7
x 3
```

8.
```
  365
- 148
```

9.
```
  43
  67
+ 35
```

10.
```
  10
x  6
```

11.
```
  6
x 2
```

13.
```
  593
- 247
```

Down

2.
```
  6
x 5
```

3.
```
  3,724
+ 2,487
```

4.
```
  873
- 457
```

5.
```
  100
x  57
```

7.
```
  75
+ 67
```

12.
```
  3
x 8
```

56

1 **Match the figure to its name.**

  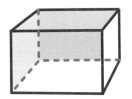 

trapezoid   rhombus   parallelogram   rectangular prism

2 **Write the numbers.**

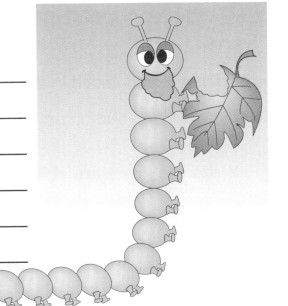

one thousand, two hundred eight ———

three thousand, seventy-five   ———

six thousand, four hundred thirty ———

nine thousand, eight hundred six ———

five thousand, six hundred forty ———

two thousand, twenty-nine   ———

3 **Write < or >.**

XVI —— X	III —— XI	II —— IX	XV —— XII
I —— VI	XII —— XX	XIV —— VIII	XIX —— XVIII
XIII —— XV	XVII —— V	IV —— VII	VI —— IV

4 **Find the product.**

X	3	4	7	1	6	0	9	5	10	2	8
2											
3											
6											
5											

5 **Find the sum and check.**

364	551	240	673	228	87	172	383
210	353	562	62	461	241	243	225
+ 194	+ 75	+ 147	+ 134	+ 170	+ 111	+ 134	+ 160

550	123	152	635	166	374	687	455
62	472	312	192	260	140	160	221
+ 243	+ 141	+ 284	+ 11	+ 111	+ 332	+ 110	+ 191

The numbers being added in an addition problem are called _____ .

The answer in an addition problem is called the _____ .

6 **Write the key word(s) in a word problem for:**

addition	subtraction
_____	_____
_____	_____
_____	_____
_____	_____

7 Mary had just finished reading Chapter XVII in her book. There were 24 chapters in the book. What chapter did she just finish? _____ How many more chapters does she need to read to finish the book? _____ Write the number of chapters in the book using Roman numerals. _____ Write in Roman numerals the chapter she would have just finished if she had read half of the chapters. _____

1 **Write the Roman numerals.**

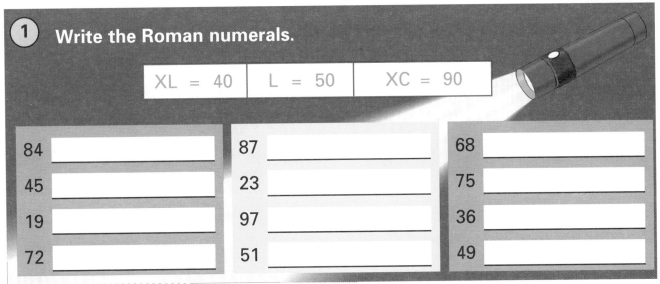

| XL = 40 | L = 50 | XC = 90 |

84 _____
45 _____
19 _____
72 _____

87 _____
23 _____
97 _____
51 _____

68 _____
75 _____
36 _____
49 _____

2 **Write the name.**

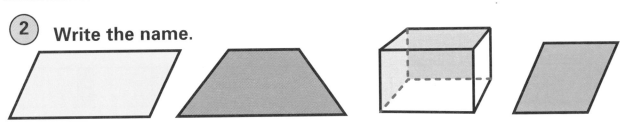

_____ _____ _____ _____

3 **Find the sum and check.**

$ 7.20	$ 9.06	$ 6.23	$ 8.14	$ 3.64	$ 3.37	$ 5.37	$ 6.24
5.29	5.77	4.19	8.49	7.28	8.18	8.12	9.03
+ 3.28	+ 1.13	+ 5.42	+ 2.36	+ 5.05	+ 2.21	+ 3.04	+ 1.27

4 **Write the word numbers.**

1,380 _____

4,076 _____

8,109 _____

2,501 _____

7,830 _____

3,402 _____

59

5 **Find the difference.**

| 5 10 |
| 6 1⁷7 |
| -2 9 8 |
| 3 1 9 |

320
- 151

442
- 268

737
- 189

516
- 237

674
- 489

413
- 268

624
- 175

753
- 687

830
- 558

651
- 176

960
- 284

624
- 578

943
- 554

820
- 395

732
- 486

6 **Find the product.**

3
x 7

6
x 4

9
x 2

2
x 6

10
x 3

7
x 6

6
x 3

3
x 5

4
x 5

2
x 8

A	D	E	G	H	I	K	N	O	R	S	W
24	12	54	27	21	20	15	48	42	18	16	30

2
x 9

9
x 6

6
x 5

8
x 3

3
x 6

4
x 3

10
x 2

6
x 8

3
x 9

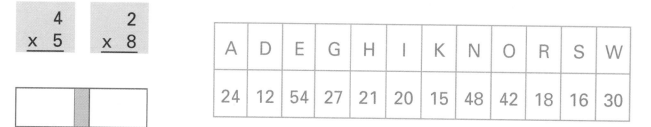

7 Mark wanted to buy a notebook for $ 2.98 and a set of baseball cards for $ 14.95. The baseball cards cost how much more than the notebook? _____ How much would they both cost? _____ Could Mark buy both for $ 20.00? ____ How much money would he have left? ____ What bills and coins would he receive for change?_____

_____

1 Match the figure to its name.

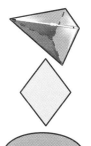

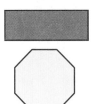

oval

triangle

octagon

pyramid

cone

diamond

circle

parallelogram

rectangle

hexagon

trapezoid

sphere

square

cylinder

pentagon

rectangular prism

rhombus

cube

2 Find the sum and check.

531	721	453	461	631	280	372	281
971	756	662	487	942	751	644	901
+ 495	+ 182	+ 633	+ 820	+ 175	+ 418	+ 851	+ 131

3 Write the Arabic numbers.

LXIV _____   XXXIX _____   LXXXI _____

XVI _____   XXXVII _____   LVIII _____

LXXXIV _____   LII _____   XXIII _____

XLVIII _____   LXXV _____   XC _____

4 Write +, -, x, or =.

3 ____ 4 = 12   14 - 9 ____ 5   14 ____ 9 = 5

7 ____ 3 = 10   6 ____ 8 = 48   12 ____ 8 = 20

61

5 Find the difference. Write the terms.

$\begin{array}{r} {\scriptstyle 8\ 10} \\ 9\ \not{9}\ 0 \\ -8\ 3\ 2 \\ \hline \end{array}$ _____ _____ _____	512 - 385	854 - 367	422 - 193	715 - 248	325 - 197

701	618	423	820	963	951	632	904
- 495	- 549	- 69	- 647	- 96	- 397	- 286	- 548

6 Find the product.

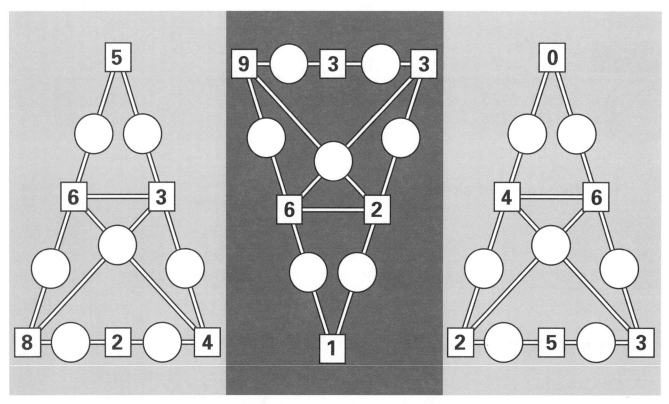

7 Write one addition and one subtraction word problem using two digit numbers. Find the answers.

_____ _____

_____ _____

_____ _____

_____ _____

_____ _____

62

1 **Circle the money needed.** 3 pts. total for this exercise.

72¢ $ 1.38 $ 1.56

2 **Write the correct time.** 5 pts. total for this exercise.

_____   _____   _____   _____   _____

3 **Solve the equations.** 4 pts. total for this exercise.

n + 3 = 12	n + 8 = 13	n + 5 = 11	n + 6 = 14

4 **Write the numbers.** 8 pts. total for this exercise.

(4 + 5) + 3 = 4 + (5 + 3)   2 + (7 + 6) = (2 + 7) + 6

____ + 3 = 4 + ____   2 + ____ = ____ + 6

____ = ____   ____ = ____

⑤ **Round the numbers to the nearest 10.** 12 pts. total for this exercise.

284 _____	573 _____	139 _____	23 _____
392 _____	846 _____	651 _____	147 _____
728 _____	417 _____	968 _____	589 _____

⑥ **Find the difference.** 8 pts. total for this exercise.

| 693 | 957 | 684 | 582 | 485 | 371 | 563 | 785 |
| - 466 | - 409 | - 167 | - 175 | - 249 | - 146 | - 147 | - 239 |

⑦ **Write the numbers.** 27 pts. total for this exercise.

3,000 + 700 + 20 + 6 = (3 x _____) + (7 x _____) + (2 x _____) + (6 x _____)

5,000 + 800 + 90 + 1 = (5 x _____) + (8 x _____) + (9 x _____) + (1 x _____)

4,000 + 200 + 50 + 7 = (4 x _____) + (2 x _____) + (5 x _____) + (7 x _____)

(5 x 1,000) + (6 x 100) + (4 x 10) + (7 x 1) = _____ + _____ + _____ + _____ = _____

(8 x 1,000) + (4 x 100) + (6 x 10) + (2 x 1) = _____ + _____ + _____ + _____ = _____

(1 x 1,000) + (0 x 100) + (3 x 10) + (6 x 1) = _____ + _____ + _____ + _____ = _____

⑧ Craig and Brandon were playing checkers. Craig won 6 more games than Brandon. Brandon won 12 games. How many games did Craig win? _____ _____ 2 pts.

José is six years younger than Juan. If Juan is 15 years old, how old is José? _____ _____ If José is 12 years old, how old is Juan? _____ _____ 4 pts.

64

73 Total pts.

	thousands				
	tens	ones	hundreds	tens	ones
	4	0	0	0	0

4 x 10,000 = 40,000

1 Write the expanded and standard numbers.

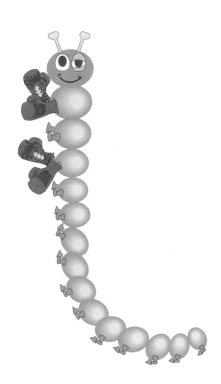

4 ten thousands = __4__ x _10,000_ = _40,000_

6 ten thousands = _____ x _____ = _____

7 ten thousands = _____ x _____ = _____

8 ten thousands = _____ x _____ = _____

5 ten thousands = _____ x _____ = _____

3 ten thousands = _____ x _____ = _____

9 ten thousands = _____ x _____ = _____

2 ten thousands = _____ x _____ = _____

2 Write the names.

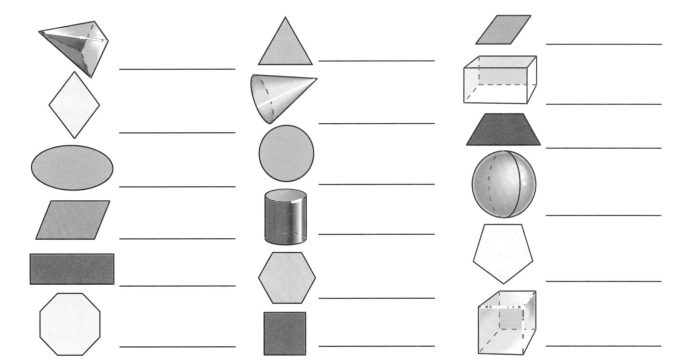

65

Find the difference. Write the terms.

836		940	654	862	615	962
- 147	_____	- 758	- 376	- 674	- 168	- 497

_____

713	643	852	972	501	710	748	830
- 587	- 585	- 587	- 388	- 259	- 252	- 399	- 275

④ **Match the fractions.**

$\frac{3}{4}$	seven-eighths	$\frac{7}{8}$	$\frac{1}{2}$	four-sixths	$\frac{3}{5}$
	three-fourths			one-half	
$\frac{2}{3}$	five-sixths	$\frac{4}{5}$	$\frac{1}{3}$	one-third	$\frac{4}{6}$
	six-sevenths			three-fifths	
$\frac{5}{6}$	two-thirds	$\frac{6}{7}$	$\frac{2}{4}$	five-eighths	$\frac{5}{8}$
	four-fifths			two-fourths	

⑤ **Write +, -, x, or =.**

3 + 8 ____ 11	15 ____ 9 = 6	2 x 8 ____ 16
5 ____ 9 = 45	7 ____ 8 = 15	10 ____ 5 = 5
4 ____ 9 = 13	13 ____ 7 = 6	2 ____ 6 = 8
12 ____ 8 = 4	4 ____ 6 = 24	7 ____ 3 = 21
6 ____ 8 = 48	11 - 6 ____ 5	5 ____ 6 = 11

⑥ **Write the missing numbers for the addition puzzle.**

4		9
	6	15

	7	
4		12
5		

3		12
	9	
11		

66

1 **Write the correct time.**

_____   _____   _____

_____   _____   _____   _____   _____

_____   _____   _____   _____   _____

2 **Write the largest number possible.**

3 8 1 0 6	7 2 5 4 9	8 2 6 9 1	3 4 0 7 5
_____	_____	_____	_____

1 6 5 7 8	2 9 0 4 3	9 5 6 0 2	3 7 4 1 8
_____	_____	_____	_____

③ Write = or ≠.

7 ten thousands ____ 7,000	6 x 1,000 ____ 6,000
5 x 10,000 ____ 50,000	20,000 ____ 2 x 10,000
30,000 ____ 3 ten thousands	4,000 ____ 4 x 1,000
8 x 10,000 ____ 8,000	9 x 10,000 ____ 9,000

④ Find the sum and check.

3,601	1,915	4,315	1,318	3,322	2,854	3,215
1,539	3,638	2,915	5,929	3,309	1,302	3,716
+ 1,247	+ 4,233	+ 2,144	+ 2,250	+ 2,855	+ 4,129	+ 1,547

⑤ Match the fractions.

$\frac{1}{4}$	two-fifths	$\frac{3}{7}$	$\frac{3}{6}$	three-eighths	$\frac{4}{7}$
	three-sevenths			four-sevenths	
$\frac{2}{5}$	one-fourth	$\frac{6}{8}$	$\frac{2}{9}$	two-ninths	$\frac{3}{8}$
	two-sixths			three-sixths	
$\frac{2}{6}$	five-ninths	$\frac{5}{9}$	$\frac{7}{12}$	seven-twelfths	$\frac{3}{11}$
	six-eighths			three-elevenths	

In the fraction $\frac{3}{4}$, the _____ tells how many parts in the whole and the _____ tells how many of the parts are being used.

⑥ Each pen at the chicken farm held 12 chickens. If there were 100 pens, how many chickens could be contained at the chicken farm?

The first grade sold 132 tickets for the school play. The second grade sold 94. Which grade sold the most tickets?_____ How many more? _____ How many did the two grades sell in all? _____ _____

1 **Write the numbers in expanded and standard form.**

forty-three thousand, two hundred seventy-five
4 ten thousands + 3 thousands + 2 hundreds + 7 tens + 5 ones =

_____ + _____ + _____ + ____ + ____ = _____

sixty-seven thousand, five hundred thirty-eight
6 ten thousands + 7 thousands + 5 hundreds + 3 tens + 8 ones =

_____ + _____ + _____ + ____ + ____ = _____

ninety thousand, six hundred two
9 ten thousands + 0 thousands + 6 hundreds + 0 tens + 2 ones =

_____ + _____ + _____ + ____ + ____ = _____

thirty-one thousand, fifty-six
3 ten thousands + 1 thousand + 0 hundreds + 5 tens + 6 ones =

_____ + _____ + _____ + ____ + ____ = _____

2 **Write the correct time.**

3 Write the smallest number possible.

1 3 5 4 2 _____ 8 0 6 9 7 _____ 2 8 4 0 6 _____ 3 5 1 9 7 _____

4 Find the sum and check.

$ 31.90	$ 28.42	$ 13.01	$ 24.35	$ 39.10	$ 21.26	$ 18.63
18.39	16.13	67.92	56.54	14.44	38.91	27.44
+ 27.20	+ 43.94	+ 15.92	+ 4.70	+ 22.95	+ 27.61	+ 23.52

5 Write the fraction words.

$\frac{4}{4}$ _____ $\frac{1}{6}$ _____

$\frac{1}{5}$ _____ $\frac{2}{7}$ _____

$\frac{5}{7}$ _____ $\frac{2}{8}$ _____

6 Find the product.

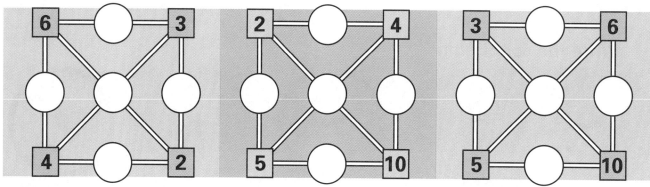

7 Write one addition and one subtraction word problem using time.
Find the answers.

_____ _____

_____ _____

_____ _____

_____ _____

1 Solve the equations.

n + 6 = 2 x 7
n + 6̸ = 14
  - 6̸   -6
_____
  n = 8
check
8 + 6 = 2 x 7
    14 = 14
	n + 3 = 4 x 6	n + 9 = 3 x 5

n + 5 = 8 x 3	n + 4 = 3 x 6	n + 7 = 6 x 8

2 Write = or ≠.

40,000 + 800 + 3,000 + 70 + 5

_____ + _____ + _____ + _____ + _____   ____   43,875

60,000 + 2,000 + 50 + 300 + 1

_____ + _____ + _____ + _____ + _____   ____   62,531

30,000 + 900 + 60 + 8,000 + 7

_____ + _____ + _____ + _____ + _____   ____   38,967

3 Find the product.

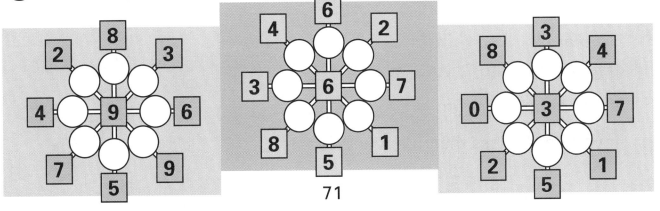

71

4 **Write the correct time.**

_____ _____ _____ _____ _____

_____ _____ _____ _____ _____

5 **Find the sum and check. Write the terms.**

172	_____	1,318	2,127	1,370	3,172
2,196	_____	1,364	4,783	8,069	2,145
+ 7,214	_____	+ 5,273	+ 2,074	+ 531	+ 2,256
	_____				

6 **Write the fraction words.**

$\frac{3}{11}$ _____ $\frac{4}{13}$ _____

$\frac{9}{14}$ _____ $\frac{8}{15}$ _____

$\frac{5}{9}$ _____ $\frac{7}{10}$ _____

7 **Who am I?**

If you add me to 7, you have 15. _____

If you subtract me from 12, you have 9. _____

If you have 8 less than me, you have 3. _____

72

1

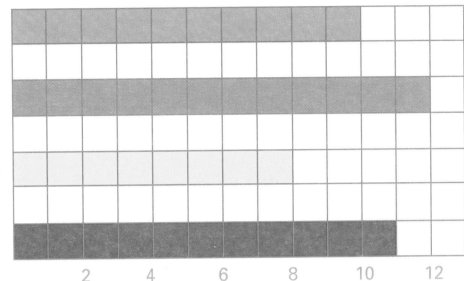

What subject has the least votes? _____

How many students chose science? _____

What is the favorite subject of the most students? _____

How many students liked social studies most? _____

How many students are in the third grade? _____

2 **Write < or >.**

863 ____ 1,432	2,425 ____ 2,245	483 ____ 480
3,284 ____ 2,843	7,063 ____ 7,603	692 ____ 6,920
5,280 ____ 5,234	4,584 ____ 4,586	257 ____ 752
6,182 ____ 6,753	9,005 ____ 8,987	516 ____ 569

3 **Who Am I?**

The sum of 24 and me is 30. _____

The difference between 16 and me is 4. _____

The product of 100 and me is 600. _____

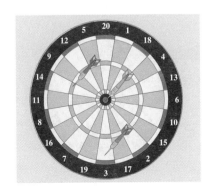

73

4 Write the correct time.

_____   _____   _____   _____   _____

5 Find the difference.

827	706	542	968	210	944	932	514
- 396	- 348	- 316	- 229	- 127	- 595	- 487	- 276

710	231	928	461	815	383	721	843
- 142	- 97	- 139	- 398	- 236	- 298	- 669	- 355

6 Find the product.

X	3	1	9	4	0	7	10	6	8	2	5
9											

7 Solve the equations.

$n + 8 = 4 \times 6$	$n + 5 = 3 \times 9$	$n + 9 = 5 \times 7$

74

① Write the numbers.

(4 + 6) + 3 = 4+(6 + 3)
  _10_ + 3 = 4+ _9_
      ____ = ____

(1 + 9) + ____ = ____ + (9 + 8)
  ____ + ____ = ____ + ____
        ____ =____

(____ + 2) + 8 = 6 + (____ + 8)
  ____ + ____ = ____ + ____
        ____ =____

2 + (7 + 5) = (2 + 7) + 5
  ____ + ____ = ____ + ____
        ____ = ____

4 + (____ +3) = (4 + 9) + ____
4 + ____ = ____ + ____
      ____ = ____

____ + (9 + 5) = (7 + 9) + ____
  ____ + ____ = ____ + ____
        ____ =____

② Write < or >.

3,842 ____ 3,482

4,753 ____ 753

6,510 ____ 6,501

8,003 ____ 8,300

2,468 ____ 2,466

5,237 ____ 5,273

③ Find the product.

④ Arrange these numbers from largest to smallest.

26	38	15	44	73	81	52	67
even				odd			
____	____	____	____	____	____	____	____

Temperature Highs

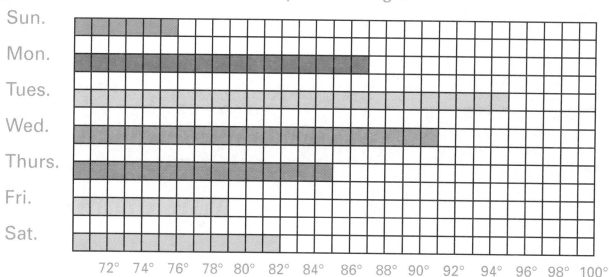

| | 72° | 74° | 76° | 78° | 80° | 82° | 84° | 86° | 88° | 90° | 92° | 94° | 96° | 98° | 100° |

On what day was it the coolest? _____ What was the temperature on

Thursday? _____ What day was it 79°? _____ What was the

temperature on Monday? _____ What days were the temperatures over

90°? _____ What day was the temperature 82°? _____

6 **Write the correct time.**

_____   _____   _____   _____   _____

7 Karen went to play at Sarah's at 9:00 A.M. She had been up two
hours. What time did she get up? _____ What time should she come
home if she was to play for three hours? _____ If she slept for two
hours after coming home, what time did she wake up? _____

   Brent was to go skating two hours before noon. What time was he to
go skating? _____ If he got home one hour after noon, what time did
he arrive home? _____ How long was Brent skating? _____

1

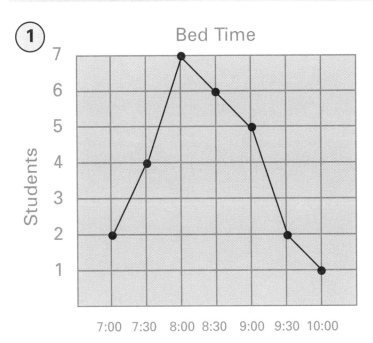

Bed Time

Students

7
6
5
4
3
2
1

7:00 7:30 8:00 8:30 9:00 9:30 10:00

How many students go to bed at 9:00? _____ How many go to bed before 8:45? _____ How many go to bed after 8:45? _____ 4 students go to bed at what time? _____ At what time do the largest number of students go to bed? _____ How many students are there in all?

_____ _____

2 **Write the numbers in expanded form.**

40,000 + 8,000 + 200 + 60 + 3 =

(____ x 10,000) + (____ x 1,000) + (____ x 100) + (____ x 10) + (____ x 1)

60,000 + 7,000 + 500 + 10 + 0 =

(____ x _____) + (____ x _____) + (____ x ____) + (____ x ___) + (____ x ___)

90,000 + 4,000 + 700 + 30 + 6 =

(____ x _____) + (____ x _____) + (____ x ____) + (____ x ___) + (____ x ___)

50,000 + 6,000 + 400 + 70 + 2 =

(____ x _____) + (____ x _____) + (____ x ____) + (____ x ___) + (____ x ___)

3 **Write the numbers.**

6,435 is between 6,430 and _____ and is closer to _____.

2,719 is between 2,710 and _____ and is closer to _____.

5,062 is between 5,060 and _____ and is closer to _____.

8,375 is between 8,370 and _____ and is closer to _____.

4 **Write the numbers.**

(2 + ____) + 1 = ____ + (6 + ____) ____ + ____ = ____ + ____ ____ = ____	____ + (7 + ____) = (4 + ____) + 3 ____ + ____ = ____ + ____ ____ = ____
5 + (8 + ____) = (____ + ____) + 9 ____ + ____ = ____ + ____ ____ = ____	(2 + ____) + ____ = ____ + (7 + 5) ____ + ____ = ____ + ____ ____ = ____

5 **Find the difference and check.**

$ 7.83 - 1.68	$ 6.17 - 4.49	$ 8.75 - 4.85	$ 9.20 - 2.69	$ 8.26 - 1.34	$ 9.62 - 7.87	$ 7.09 - 3.55	$ 4.26 - 2.83

$ 8.60 - 2.76	$ 7.95 - 5.37	$ 6.23 - 1.90	$ 5.04 - 1.87	$ 4.28 - 2.58	$ 2.13 - .85	$ 5.64 - 1.79	$ 8.94 - 2.56

6 **Solve the equations.**

n + 3 = 6 x 8	n + 5 = 3 x 7	n + 9 = 4 x 9

7 **Write even or odd.**

days in a week _____		dimes in a half dollar _____
months in a year _____		dimes in a dollar _____
days in January _____		pennies in a quarter _____
days in June _____		minutes in an hour _____
number in a dozen _____		weeks in a year _____

78

1

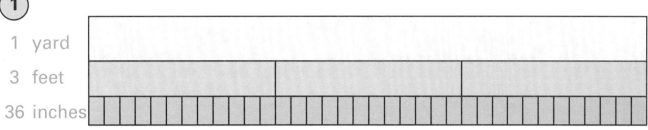

1 yard

3 feet

36 inches

1 yard (yd.) = 3 feet (ft.) = 36 inches (in.)
12 inches (in.) = 1 foot (ft.)

1 _____ = 36 inches   1 foot = _____ inches

1 _____ = 12 inches   1 yard = _____ inches

1 _____ = 3 feet   1 yard = _____ feet

2

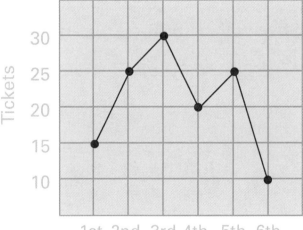

Tickets Sold to the Play

Tickets

30
25
20
15
10

1st 2nd 3rd 4th 5th 6th

What grade sold the most tickets?

_____ What 2 grades sold the same

number? _____ How many did the 4th

grade sell? _____ What grade sold 15

tickets? _____ What grade sold the

least tickets? _____ How many tickets

where sold altogether? _____ _____

3 **Write the numbers.**

6,834 is between _____ and 6,840 and is closer to _____.

2,755 is between _____ and 2,760 and is closer to _____.

5,219 is between _____ and 5,220 and is closer to _____.

8,395 is between _____ and 8,400 and is closer to _____.

3,147 is between _____ and 3,150 and is closer to _____.

(4) **Solve the equations.**

n + 10 = 6 x 7	n + 13 = 5 x 4	n + 12 = 3 x 8

(5)

Is $ 5.00 enough money to buy the ball and bat? _____ How much change

will you receive if you buy the doll with $ 10.00? _____ How much more

money do you need if you have saved $ 3.75 toward the teddy bear?

_____ Can you buy the ball, bat, and ball glove with $ 15.00 ? _____ How

much more do you need? _____

(6) **Write the numbers.**

(6 + 4) + ____ = 6 + (____+ 3) ____ + ____ = ____ +____ ____ = ____	____ + (8 + 1) = (2 + 8) + ____ ____ + ____ = ____ + ____ ____ = ____

(7) **Write the numbers in expanded form.**

90,000 + 50 + 700 + 1 + 6,000 = _____ + _____ + _____ + _____ + _____ =

(____ x _____) + (____ x _____) + (____ x _____) + (____ x ____) + (____ x ____)

3,000 + 400 + 20,000 + 8 + 90 = _____ + _____ + _____ + _____ + _____ =

(____ x _____) + (____ x _____) + (____ x _____) + (____ x ____) = (____ x ____)

```
 tens ones          23 is 2 tens  +    3 ones        short cut
  2   3                        x 2                        23
  x  2                         ──────                    x  2
                     6 (2 x 3 ones)                      ────
                    40     (2 x 2 tens)                   46
                    ────
                    46                       multiply 2 times ones
                                             multiply 2 times tens
```

1 **Find the product. Write the terms.**

21	_____	22	21	32	12	31	12
x 4	_____	x 2	x 3	x 2	x 2	x 2	x 3

_____

20	22	12	23	20	21	22	30	34
x 4	x 4	x 4	x 3	x 2	x 2	x 3	x 3	x 2

2 **Write the number of coins and bills needed to buy each.**

$4.36 $5.42 $8.75 $72.89

$ 10	_____	_____	_____	_____
$ 5	_____	_____	_____	_____
$ 1	_____	_____	_____	_____
50¢	_____	_____	_____	_____
25¢	_____	_____	_____	_____
10¢	_____	_____	_____	_____
5¢	_____	_____	_____	_____
1¢	_____	_____	_____	_____

3 **Write +, -, x, or =.**

8 ____ 3 = 24	8 - 3 ____ 5	8 ____ 3 = 11
6 ____ 5 = 1	6 ____ 5 = 30	6 ____ 5 = 11
9 ____ 7 = 16	9 ____ 7 = 2	9 x 7 ____ 63

81

Bicycles Sold

April	🚲 🚲 🚲
May	🚲 🚲 🚲 🚲 🚲
June	🚲 🚲 🚲 🚲 🚲 🚲 🚲 🚲
July	🚲 🚲 🚲 🚲
August	🚲

🚲 represents 10 bicycles

The month with the most bicycle sales is _____. How many were sold that month? _____ In what month were 40 bicycles sold? _____ What month had the least bicycles sold? _____ How many were sold in May? _____ How many more were sold in July than in April? _____ How many bicycles were sold in all? _____ _____

5 **Write the numbers.**

1 yd. = _____ in.   1 yd. = _____ ft.   1 ft. = _____ in.

6 **Write the numbers.**

7,203 is between _____ and _____ and is closer to _____.

4,165 is between _____ and _____ and is closer to _____.

3,926 is between _____ and _____ and is closer to _____.

5,642 is between _____ and _____ and is closer to _____.

9,397 is between _____ and _____ and is closer to _____.

7 At the bakery a dozen donut holes were $ 0.78, a dozen bagels were $ 1.60, a loaf of bread was $ 0.99, and a dozen cookies were $ 2.43. How many donut holes are in a dozen?_____ How much would a dozen bagels and a dozen donut holes cost? _____ What would it cost to buy a dozen cookies and a loaf of bread? _____ What two things could be bought with $ 2.00? _____ _____ Could a dozen donut holes, a dozen cookies, and a loaf of bread be bought with $ 4.00? _____

(1) **Write the numbers.**

seventy-two thousand, four hundred fifty-nine _____

thirty-six thousand, one hundred forty-eight _____

fifty thousand, six hundred twenty-seven _____

eighteen thousand, nine hundred three _____

forty-one thousand, seventy-five _____

sixty-seven thousand, three hundred fifteen _____

(2)

Nuts Collected

Acorns	🌰	🌰	🌰	🌰						
Hazel	●	●								
Hickory	●	●	●	●	●					
Walnuts	●	●	●	●	●	●	●			
Pecans	●	●	●	●	●	●	●	●	●	●

● represents 5 lbs. of nuts

How many pounds of hickory nuts were collected? _____ _____ How many

pounds of walnuts were collected? _____ _____ There were 10 pounds

of_____ collected. How many pounds of hazel nuts and acorns were

collected? _____ _____ More _____ were collected than any other kind of nut.

(3) **Find the product. Write the terms.**

43	_____	14	11	22	10	12	13
x 2	_____	x 2	x 8	x 2	x 2	x 4	x 3

_____

22	20	13	32	21	44	12	11	10
x 4	x 3	x 2	x 3	x 3	x 2	x 3	x 5	x 3

(4) Round the numbers to the nearest 10.

5,124 is closer to _____   4,568 is closer to _____   1,746 is closer to _____

8,375 is closer to _____   7,283 is closer to _____   3,451 is closer to _____

(5) Measure the lines with an inch ruler.

_____ _____

_____ _____

(6) Write the Roman numerals.

1 _____	10 _____	100 _____
2 _____	20 _____	200 _____
3 _____	30 _____	300 _____
4 _____	40 _____	400 _____
5 _____	50 _____	500 _____
6 _____	60 _____	600 _____
7 _____	70 _____	700 _____
8 _____	80 _____	800 _____
9 _____	90 _____	900 _____

(7) Joan's ribbon is 15 inches long. Is her ribbon longer or shorter than a foot? _____ By how much? _____

From San Francisco to Chicago is two thousand, one hundred seventy-three miles. From Denver to Miami is two thousand, one hundred seven miles. From Chicago to New York is eight hundred nine miles. Which would be the shortest trip?_____
From Denver to Miami is how much longer than from Chicago to New York? _____ _____ How far is it from San Francisco to New York by way of Chicago? _____ _____

1 **Match the figure to its name.** 18 pts. total for this exercise.

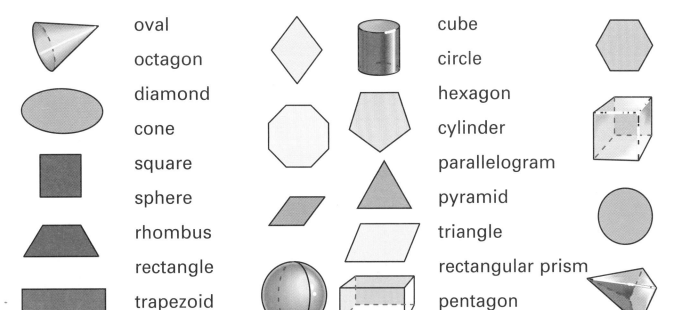

oval

octagon

diamond

cone

square

sphere

rhombus

rectangle

trapezoid

cube

circle

hexagon

cylinder

parallelogram

pyramid

triangle

rectangular prism

pentagon

2 **Write the Arabic numbers.** 9 pts. total for this exercise.

LXXXVI _____   XLVIII _____   LIV _____

XIX _____   XCIII _____   XXI _____

LXXV _____   XXXVII _____   LXII _____

3 **Write = or ≠.** 5 pts. total for this exercise.

one thousand, eight hundred thirty-four _____ 1,834

five thousand, two hundred seventy-nine _____ 5,792

six thousand, three hundred five _____ 6,305

nine thousand, one hundred eighty-seven _____ 9,187

three thousand, four hundred twenty _____ 3,402

4 **Find the sum and check.** 8 pts. total for this exercise.

145	127	263	356	253	243	628	257
270	345	495	155	465	584	236	443
+ 371	+ 501	+ 129	+ 84	+ 155	+ 147	+ 112	+ 196

5 Members in Family   5 pts. total for this exercise.

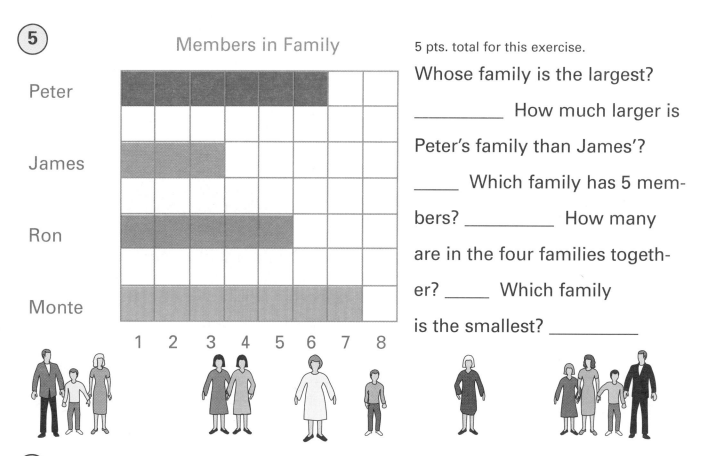

Whose family is the largest? _____ How much larger is Peter's family than James'? _____ Which family has 5 members? _____ How many are in the four families together? _____ Which family is the smallest? _____

6 Becky has 32 subtraction facts to solve. If she has solved 18 of them, how many more does she have to solve? 1 pt.

If Francis starts lunch at 12:10 P.M. and must finish by 12:50 P.M., how long is her lunch time? 1 pt.

Chip installed 128 square yards of carpeting on Monday, 202 on Tuesday, and 179 on Wednesday. How many square yards of carpeting did he install in all? 1 pt.

7 **Find the product.** 24 pts.

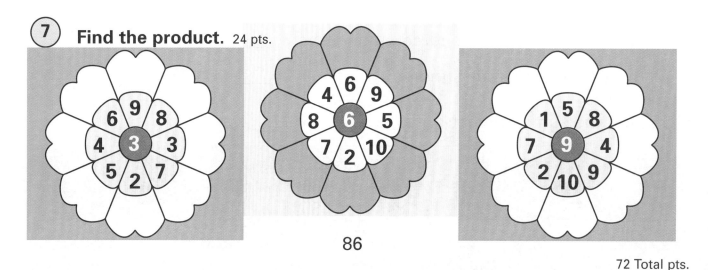

72 Total pts.

(1) Write the Roman numerals.

53	_____	87	_____	60	_____
49	_____	16	_____	38	_____
25	_____	42	_____	61	_____
74	_____	94	_____	9	_____

(2) Round the numbers to the nearest 10.

5,286 _____	4,152 _____	2,367 _____	1,365 _____
1,739 _____	7,045 _____	6,821 _____	4,789 _____
8,273 _____	3,698 _____	9,574 _____	6,103 _____

(3) Write the word numbers.

34,086 _____

72,159 _____

56,402 _____

48,825 _____

23,734 _____

60,273 _____

81,567 _____

(4) Write +, -, or x.

more than	_____	less than	_____
and	_____	product	_____
left	_____	difference	_____
altogether	_____	both	_____
in all	_____	sum	_____

5 Find the product. Write the terms.

22 x 2	_____ _____ _____	23 x 3	33 x 3	21 x 3	42 x 2	22 x 4	13 x 2

| 43
x 2 | 44
x 2 | 21
x 4 | 34
x 2 | 41
x 2 | 32
x 2 | 22
x 3 | 32
x 3 | 23
x 2 |

6 Find the sum and check.

| 1,332
8,559
+ 406 | 1,042
5,457
+ 2,330 | 7,217
9,018
+ 3,613 | 3,750
1,418
+ 4,621 | 2,636
1,660
+ 4,283 | 6,281
1,579
+ 3,014 | 6,245
1,370
+ 8,591 |

7 Find the difference and check.

| 783
- 654 | 939
- 479 | 681
- 595 | 725
- 448 | 472
- 338 | 938
- 690 | 549
- 368 | 726
- 438 |

| 513
- 476 | 658
- 397 | 641
- 189 | 914
- 39 | 759
- 162 | 586
- 239 | 714
- 265 | 641
- 559 |

8 Who Am I?

When I am taken from 16, the result is 12. _____

When I have 8 added to me, the result is 18. _____

When 9 is subtracted from me, the result is 15. _____

When I am decreased by 6, the result is 7. _____

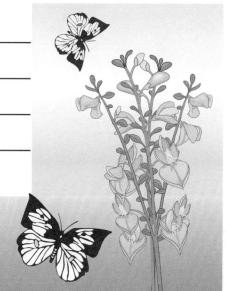

$\frac{4}{10}$ fraction

0.4   decimal

four-tenths   word number

hundreds	tens	ones	tenths		
		0 .	4		

(1) **Write the fraction as a decimal and read it.**

$\frac{2}{10}$ _____ $\frac{7}{10}$ _____ $\frac{5}{10}$ _____ $\frac{8}{10}$ _____ $\frac{4}{10}$ _____

(2) **Write the fractional part that is shaded. Arrange the fractions smallest to largest in the second row of blanks.**

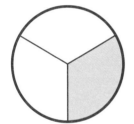 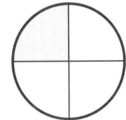 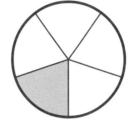 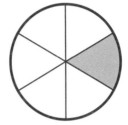 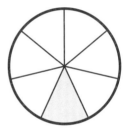

_____   _____   _____   _____   _____

_____   _____   _____   _____   _____

(3) **Find the product.**

52	74	32	52	34	72	61	63	72
x 3	x 2	x 4	x 3	x 2	x 3	x 4	x 2	x 4

82	63	31	40	51	64	83	90	62
x 3	x 3	x 6	x 7	x 6	x 2	x 2	x 5	x 3

4 Draw the outline of each shape or solid.

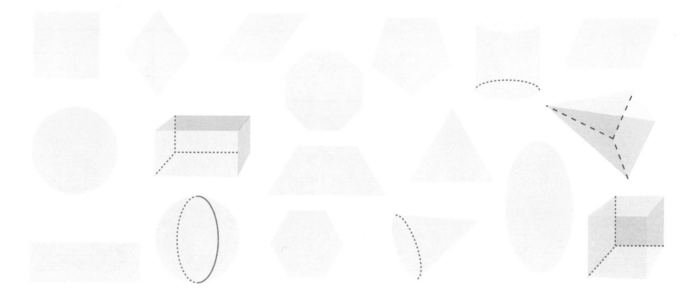

5 Solve the equations and check.

$n + 4 = 13 - 6$	$n + 2 = 15 - 8$	$n + 5 = 12 - 4$

6 Write the Roman numerals.

34 _____	73 _____	98 _____
47 _____	69 _____	52 _____
11 _____	26 _____	85 _____

7 Mother was making 7 blouses for the cheerleaders. There were 6 buttons on each blouse. How many buttons did she need? _____ _____
She found 7 buttons in her button box. How many more must she buy? _____

Henry spent 8 weeks playing basketball. How many days did he play basketball? _____ _____ He played about how many months? _____ _____

90

1 Write = or ≠.

XLVI ____ 44	XVI ____ 16	XXI ____ 25
XXIX ____ 29	LXXXVIII ____ 78	LXI ____ 61
LXXIII ____ 83	LXI ____ 59	XCVII ____ 97
XXXII ____ 32	IV ____ 4	LXXI ____ 72

2 Write the fractional part that is shaded. Arrange the fractions largest to smallest in the second row of blanks.

  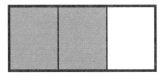 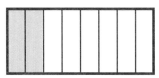

____   ____   ____   ____

____   ____   ____   ____

3 Write the decimal part that is shaded. Read the decimal.

 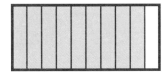 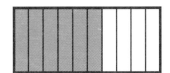 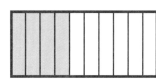

____   ____   ____   ____

4 Solve the equations and check.

n + 3 = 15 - 6	n + 6 = 14 - 8	n + 4 = 11 - 5

91

5 Write the names of the figures. Match the figures.

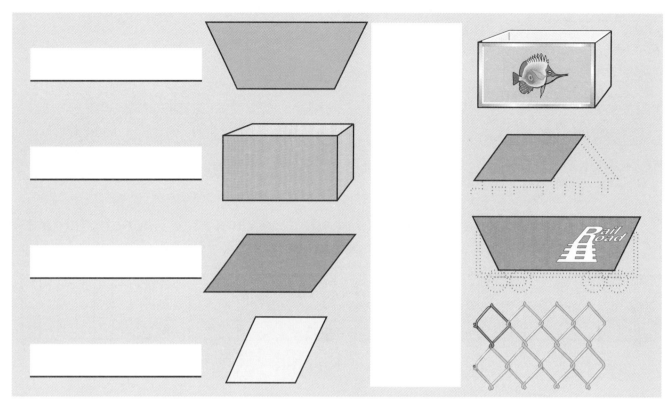

_____

_____

_____

_____

6 Find the product.

73	81	43	62	42	23	63	22	64
x 2	x 6	x 3	x 4	x 3	x 2	x 2	x 4	x 2

90	54	93	32	53	72	82	33	82
x 7	x 2	x 2	x 4	x 3	x 2	x 4	x 3	x 3

7 Write one addition and one subtraction word problem. Find the answers.

_____   _____

_____   _____

_____   _____

_____   _____

_____   _____

$\dfrac{3}{4}$ _____ number of parts used

_____ number of parts in the whole

(1) **Arrange the fractions from smallest to largest.**

$\dfrac{1}{8}$ $\dfrac{1}{4}$ $\dfrac{1}{7}$ $\dfrac{1}{2}$ $\dfrac{1}{10}$ $\dfrac{1}{5}$ $\dfrac{1}{9}$ $\dfrac{1}{3}$ $\dfrac{1}{6}$

___ ___ ___ ___ ___ ___ ___ ___ ___

(2) **Match the figure to its name.**

rectangular prism   rhombus   parallelogram   trapezoid

(3) **Find the product.**

10	9	5	7	4	8	9	6	3
x 8	x 3	x 8	x 9	x 9	x 0	x 5	x 8	x 4

9	8	9	9	8	8	4	7	8
x 6	x 1	x 9	x 8	x 4	x 8	x 7	x 8	x 2

(4) **Write the word numbers.**

0.8 _____	0.7 _____
0.3 _____	0.1 _____
0.2 _____	0.9 _____
0.6 _____	0.5 _____

⑤ Write the Arabic numbers.

XXXIX _____   XXIII _____   XCIV _____

XV _____   LXXVII _____   XLII _____

LXXXVIII _____   LI _____   LXVI _____

⑥ Solve the equations and check.

n + 5 = 13 - 8   n + 8 = 16 - 4   n + 4 = 11 - 3

⑦ Find the difference and check.

420	751	803	817	609	630	924	538
- 171	- 622	- 135	- 463	- 241	- 597	- 438	- 264

⑧
Gene picked 521 oranges from the orchard on Monday. He sold 375 at the fruit stand. How many oranges did he have left? _____ _____ If he picked 263 on Tuesday and sold none of them, how many oranges did he then have altogether? _____ _____

In the appliance store, a new washing machine cost $429, a new dryer cost $389, and a new refrigerator cost $620. The washing machine costs how much more than the dryer? _____ What appliance is the most expensive? _____ How much would the washing machine and the dryer cost together? _____ Could you buy the washing machine and the refrigerator with $1,000? _____

94

1 **Write the numbers in expanded and standard form.**

5 ten thousands + 3 thousands + 7 hundreds + 2 tens + 8 ones =

(___ x _____) + (___ x _____) + (___ x _____) + (___ x ___) + (___ x ___)

_____ + _____ + _____ + _____ + _____ = _____

9 ten thousands + 4 thousands + 0 hundreds + 1 ten + 6 ones =

(___ x _____) + (___ x _____) + (___ x _____) + (___ x ___) + (___ x ___)

_____ + _____ + _____ + _____ + _____ = _____

7 ten thousands + 6 thousands + 3 hundreds + 9 tens + 2 ones =

(___ x _____) + (___ x _____) + (___ x _____) + (___ x ___) + (___ x ___)

_____ + _____ + _____ + _____ + _____ = _____

3 ten thousands + 8 thousands + 4 hundreds + 5 tens + 1 one =

(___ x _____) + (___ x _____) + (___ x _____) + (___ x ___) + (___ x ___)

_____ + _____ + _____ + _____ + _____ = _____

2 **Write the name of each figure.**

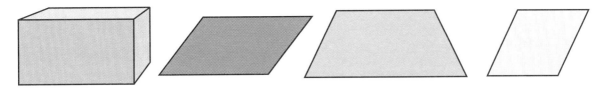

_____ _____ _____ _____

3 **Find the product.**

X	5	2	9	7	1	0	4	8	3	6	10
8											

95

4 Write < or >.

12,284 ____ 45,276		57,324 ____ 56,134		84,356 ____ 83,456	
73,567 ____ 83,190		29,743 ____ 29,473		45,276 ____ 45,267	
68,905 ____ 32,068		91,680 ____ 91,699		63,284 ____ 63,824	

5 The _____ tells how many parts of the whole are used.

The _____ tells into how many parts the whole is divided.

Arrange the fractions from largest to smallest.

$\frac{2}{3}$ $\frac{2}{6}$ $\frac{2}{8}$ $\frac{2}{10}$ $\frac{2}{5}$ $\frac{2}{9}$ $\frac{2}{4}$ $\frac{2}{11}$ $\frac{2}{7}$

____   ____   ____   ____   ____   ____   ____   ____   ____

6 Write +, -, or x.

How many apples are left? _____ How many cars in all? _____ What is the sum of the grocery list? _____ Jack has how many more pencils than Ron? _____ Mary and Suzie have how many books altogether? _____ Josh and Joe have how many trucks? _____ What is the product of 4 and 8? _____ Kerry has how many less marbles than Ken? _____

7 Find the sum.

36 + 10 = _____	58 + 10 = _____	370 + 10 = _____
128 + 10 = _____	162 + 10 = _____	825 + 10 = _____
456 + 10 = _____	365 + 10 = _____	4,176 + 10 = _____
1,279 + 10 = _____	3,127 + 10 = _____	970 + 10 = _____

1 In the fraction $\frac{3}{4}$, the denominator is a ____ and the numerator is a ____.

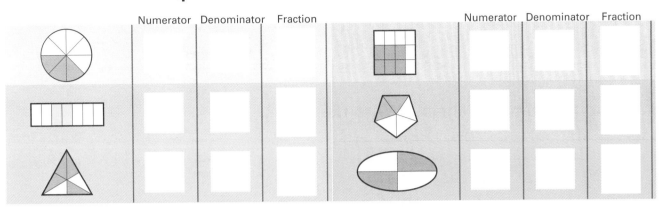

	Numerator	Denominator	Fraction		Numerator	Denominator	Fraction

2 **Write the numbers in expanded and standard form.**

4 ten thousands + 7 thousands + 5 hundreds + 2 tens + 8 ones =

(___ x _____) + (___ x _____) + (___ x ____) + (___ x ___) + (___ x ___)

_____ + _____ + ____ + ____ + ____ = _____

8 hundreds + 3 thousands + 1 ten + 6 ten thousands + 0 ones =

(___ x _____) + (___ x _____) + (___ x ____) + (___ x ___) + (___ x ___)

_____ + _____ + ____ + ____ + ____ = _____

6 thousands + 5 tens + 2 ten thousands + 0 hundreds + 7 ones =

(___ x _____) + (___ x _____) + (___ x ____) + (___ x ___) + (___ x ___)

_____ + _____ + ____ + ____ + ____ = _____

3 **Find the product.**

123	622	823	232	321	222	333	632	413
x 2	x 4	x 2	x 3	x 4	x 4	x 3	x 2	x 3

223	731	231	121	322	513	911	712	501
x 2	x 3	x 3	x 4	x 3	x 3	x 7	x 4	x 6

4 Write < or >.

15,186 ____ 35,186	73,198 ____ 73,189	27,361 ____ 27,316
42,739 ____ 47,390	30,175 ____ 30,715	54,089 ____ 54,088
62,540 ____ 62,450	82,649 ____ 86,492	93,172 ____ 91,372

5 Find the sum and check. Write the terms.

214	_____	313	214	143	311	523
342	_____	431	301	720	490	274
129	_____	383	264	422	779	836
+ 881	_____	+ 319	+ 434	+ 356	+ 204	+ 102
	_____					

6 Write = or ≠.

69 + 10 ____ 690	126 + 10 ____ 1,260
243 + 10 ____ 233	1,260 + 10 ____ 1,270
75 + 10 ____ 85	5,270 + 10 ____ 5,280
810 + 10 ____ 820	38 + 10 ____ 48
457 + 10 ____ 458	4,280 + 10 ____ 42,890

7 Find the answer.

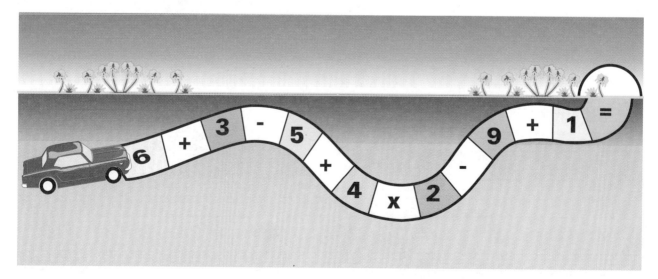

98

1 **Write the correct time.**

_____ _____ _____ _____ _____

2 **Find the product.**

532	714	422	623	912	404	833	801	313
x 3	x 2	x 4	x 2	x 3	x 2	x 3	x 4	x 3

3 **Write the numbers in expanded form.**

16,874 = _____ + _____ + _____ + ____ + ____ =

(____ x _____) + (____ x _____) + (____ x _____) + (____ x ___) + (____ x ___)

53,290 = _____ + _____ + _____ + ____ + ____ =

(____ x _____) + (____ x _____) + (____ x _____) + (____ x ___) + (____ x ___)

27,836 = _____ + _____ + _____ + ____ + ____ =

(____ x _____) + (____ x _____) + (____ x _____) + (____ x ___) + (____ x ___)

45,901 = _____ + _____ + _____ + ____ + ____ =

(____ x _____) + (____ x _____) + (____ x _____) + (____ x ___) + (____ x ___)

4 **Measure the lines with an inch ruler.**

____ _____

____ _____

99

5 Draw a bar graph.

Favorite Sports

Football   6   students

Baseball   10   students

Basketball 7   students

Soccer   3   students

6 Write the numbers.

$4 + (6 + 3) = ($____ $+$ ____$) +$ ____

____ $+$ ____ $=$ ____ $+$ ____

____ $=$ ____

$(7 + 2) + 5 =$ ____ $+ ($____ $+$ ____$)$

____ $+$ ____ $=$ ____ $+$ ____

____ $=$ ____

7 Write the numbers.

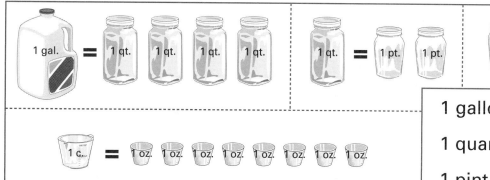

1 gallon = _____ quarts

1 quart = _____ pints

1 pint   = _____ cups

1 cup   = _____ ounces

8 Solve the equations.

$n + 8 = 4 + (3 + 7)$ $n + 8 = 4 + $ _____	$n + 5 = (3 + 2) + 6$ $n + 5 = $ _____ $+ 6$	$n + 7 = 4 + (5 + 2)$ $n + 7 = 4 + $ _____

1 **Circle the number needed.**

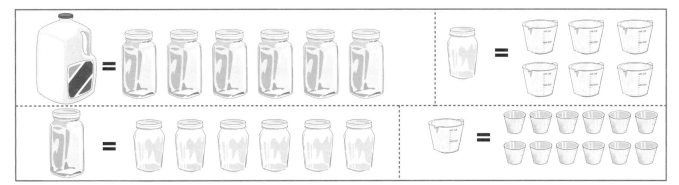

2 **Draw a bar graph.**

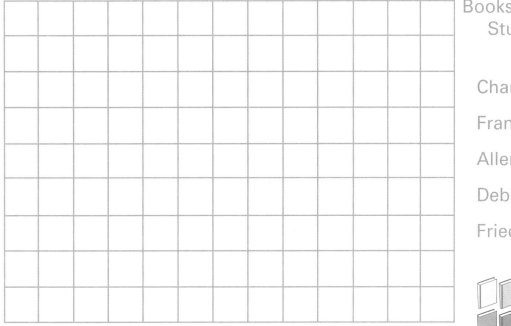

Books Read by
Students

Chang	5
Francis	8
Allen	4
Debbie	10
Frieda	12

3 **Write the numbers.**

32,485 = _____ + _____ + _____ + ____ + ____ =

(___ x _____) + (___ x _____) + (___ x ____) + (___ x ___) + (___ x ___)

75,384 = _____ + _____ + _____ + ____ + ____ =

(___ x _____) + (___ x _____) + (___ x ____) + (___ x ___) + (___ x ___)

94,387 = _____ + _____ + _____ + ____ + ____ =

(___ x _____) + (___ x _____) + (___ x ____) + (___ x ___) + (___ x ___)

4 **Write the correct time.**

_____   _____   _____   _____   _____

5 **Solve the equations.**

$n + 4 = (7 + 1) + 8$	$n + 9 = 3 + (6 + 5)$	$n + 5 = 9 + (3 + 7)$

6 **Write the numbers.**

____ + (____ + ____) = (4 + 1) + 9	(____ + ____) + ____ = 5 + (3 + 7)
____ + (____ + ____) = (2 + 8) + 6	(____ + ____) + ____ = 1 + (3 + 8)

7 Peter needs 8 boards each 4 inches long to make a fence for his train display. If he cuts them out of one board, what length board must he buy? _____ _____ Is the board longer or shorter than a yard? _____ By how much? _____ _____

The sides of a triangular backyard are 17 yards, 13 yards, and 25 yards long. How many yards of fencing will be needed to build a fence around the backyard?

102

1 **Write the numbers in expanded and standard form.**

(4 x 10,000) + (7 x 1,000) + (3 x 100) + (6 x 10) + (1 x 1) =

_____ + _____ + _____ + ____ + ____ = _____

(2 x 10,000) + (8 x 10) + (9 x 100) + (2 x 1,000) + (7 x 1) =

_____ + _____ + _____ + ____ + ____ = _____

(3 x 10,000) + (5 x 100) + (4 x 1,000) + (0 x 1) + (6 x 10) =

_____ + _____ + _____ + ____ + ____ = _____

2 **Draw a line graph.**

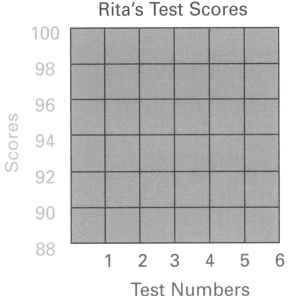

Rita's Test Scores

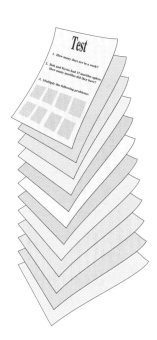

Test 1   96

Test 2   98

Test 3   94

Test 4   100

Test 5   88

Test 6   90

3 **Write the fractional part that is shaded. Write the fraction as a decimal and read it.**

____   ____   ____   ____   ____   ____

____   ____   ____   ____   ____   ____

103

4) Write the correct time.

_____ _____ _____ _____ _____

_____ _____ _____ _____ _____

5) Solve the equations.

n + 5 = (7 + 2) + 4	n + 8 = 1 + (6 + 8)	n + 6 = 1 + (4 + 5)

6) Write the numbers.

1 gal. = _____ qt.   1 qt. = _____ pt.   1 pt. = _____ c.   1 c. = _____ oz.

7) Find the difference.

9,865 - 9,348	6,982 - 3,305	4,956 - 2,839	7,891 - 2,658	7,497 - 5,379	9,571 - 6,112	7,245 - 3,018

104

1   **Write the numbers.**

3 dimes   = _____ nickels   = _____ pennies

2 quarters   = _____ dimes   = _____ nickels

               = _____ pennies

2 half dollars = _____ quarters   = _____ dimes

               = _____ nickels   = _____ pennies

8 nickels   = _____ dimes   = _____ pennies

50 pennies   = _____ half dollars = _____ quarters

               = _____ dimes   = _____ nickels

2   **Write the correct time.**

_____   _____   _____   _____   _____

3   **Write the numbers in expanded and standard form.**

(2 x 10,000) + (5 x 100) + (6 x 1,000) + (3 x 1) + (9 x 10)

_____ + _____ + _____ + ____ + ____ = _____

(4 x 100) + (1 x 10,000) + (7 x 1,000) + (0 x 10) + (8 x 1)

_____ + _____ + _____ + ____ + ____ = _____

(3 x 10) + (7 x 1,000) + (9 x 1) + (2 x 10,000) + (5 x 100)

_____ + _____ + _____ + ____ + ____ = _____

4   **Draw a line graph.**

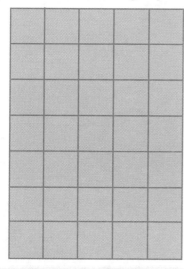

Average Snowfall

Month	Inches
Dec.	18
Jan.	24
Feb.	28
March	20

5   **Find the difference. Write the terms.**

```
  3,685        _____
- 2,176        _____
               _____
```

```
  8,353         8,794         6,326         7,890
- 8,107       - 2,706       -   317       - 4,524
```

6   **Write the decimal equivalent and word number.**

$\frac{3}{10}$ = _____ = _____ $\frac{2}{10}$ = _____ = _____

$\frac{5}{10}$ = _____ = _____ $\frac{8}{10}$ = _____ = _____

$\frac{9}{10}$ = _____ = _____ $\frac{1}{10}$ = _____ = _____

7   **Write one subtraction and one multiplication word problem. Find the answers.**

_____   _____

_____   _____

_____   _____

_____   _____

1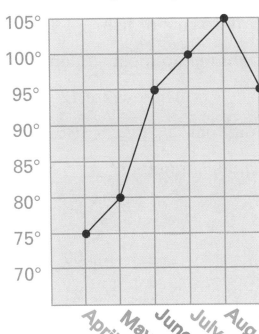

Average Temperature

7 pts. total for this exercise.

What was the average temperature in May? _____ What 2 months had the same average temperature? _____ and _____ What was the hottest month? _____ What month had an average temperature of 100°? _____ From what month to what month did the average temperature increase 15°? _____ to _____

2 **Find the difference.** 8 pts. total for this exercise.

| 924
- 264 | 871
- 859 | 841
- 675 | 603
- 280 | 535
- 489 | 341
- 123 | 670
- 542 | 758
- 293 |

3 **Solve the equations.** 3 pts. total for this exercise.

| n + 3 = 6 + 4 | n + 8 = 7 + 5 | n + 10 = 8 + 7 |

4 **Round the numbers to the nearest 10.** 9 pts. total for this exercise.

38 _____	271 _____	2,755 _____
92 _____	653 _____	5,646 _____
45 _____	849 _____	7,304 _____

5

Student's Pets   6 pts.

Dog	🐕 🐕 🐕 🐕 🐕
Cat	🐈 🐈 🐈 🐈
Bird	🐦 🐦
Fish	🐟 🐟 🐟
Hamster	🐹 🐹

each animal equals 3 pets

How many birds do the students have? _____ Are there more cats or fish? _____ Which animal do most students have? _____ There were 12 of what animal?_____ How many pets altogether? _____ _____

6 **Write < or >.** 4 pts. total for this exercise.

ten thousand, seven hundred six _____ 10,760

forty-two thousand, three hundred fifty-one _____ 40,351

seven thousand, eight hundred forty-six _____ 70,846

sixty-one thousand, four hundred thirty-nine _____ 60,439

7 **Write the numbers in expanded form.** 30 pts. total for this exercise.

32,756 = _____ + _____ + _____ + ____ + ____ =

(___ x _____) + (___ x _____) + (___ x _____) + (___ x ___) + (___ x ___)

84,190 = _____ + _____ + _____ + ____ + ____ =

(___ x _____) + (___ x _____) + (___ x _____) + (___ x ___) + (___ x ___)

8

 $3.59    $1.68    $2.87    $4.25

How much will an apple pie and a half gallon of ice cream cost? _____ A gallon of milk costs how much more than a bunch of bananas? _____ What could you buy with $ 6.00? _____ How much money would you receive back if you gave $5.00 to buy an apple pie? _____ 4 pts.

108

(1) Draw a pictograph.

Tickets Sold by 3rd Grade

Mon.   60
Tues.   40
Wed.   30
Thurs. 50
Fri.   60

each represents 10 tickets

(2) Find the product.

2,324	8,312	4,123	7,324	5,021	6,110	9,102
x 2	x 2	x 3	x 2	x 4	x 3	x 4

(3) Write +, -, or x.

3 ___ 4 = 8 ___ 4   5 ___ 3 = 10 ___ 8   6 ___ 9 = 8 ___ 7

12 ___ 8 = 5 ___ 4   9 ___ 2 = 4 ___ 3   16 ___ 6 = 5 ___ 2

(4) Write the numbers.

+	5	36	472	5,689
10				

+	570	6	7,132	84
10				

(5) Find the difference. Write the terms.

7,250   _____
- 5,226   _____

          _____

7,853	6,423	8,672	9,835
- 2,049	- 6,106	- 3,034	- 4,117

5,851	3,897	9,692	7,164	7,940	9,756	6,475
- 3,704	- 3,588	- 1,468	- 7,025	- 4,239	- 148	- 2,147

6 **Write the numbers.**

= _____ half dollars = _____ quarters
= _____ dimes = _____ nickels = _____ pennies

= _____ half dollars = _____ quarters
= _____ dimes = _____ nickels = _____ pennies

= _____ half dollars = _____ dimes = _____ pennies

= _____ half dollars = _____ dimes = _____ pennies

7 **Write the correct letter in the blank.**

‾‾‾ ‾‾‾ ‾‾‾   ‾‾‾ ‾‾‾ ‾‾‾ ‾‾‾ ‾‾‾ ‾‾‾ ‾‾‾
56 42 40   24 12 16 72 45 40 28

‾‾‾ ‾‾‾ ‾‾‾   ‾‾‾ ‾‾‾ ‾‾‾ ‾‾‾ ‾‾‾ ‾‾‾ ‾‾‾ ‾‾‾
20 12 72   24 20 16 54 36 24 18 42

F	H	D	E	L
8 x 3 =	6 x 6 =	8 x 5 =	9 x 8 =	6 x 7 =

R	U	A	T	I
3 x 4 =	6 x 3 =	5 x 4 =	6 x 9 =	4 x 4 =

N	O	S
5 x 9 =	8 x 7 =	4 x 7 =

110

1 **Write the numbers.**

15,284 is between 15,280 and _____ and is closer to _____.

28,372 is between 28,370 and _____ and is closer to _____.

72,538 is between 72,530 and _____ and is closer to _____.

56,145 is between 56,140 and _____ and is closer to _____.

83,757 is between 83,750 and _____ and is closer to _____.

2 **Write the numbers.**

 = _____ quarters + _____ nickels

 = _____ quarters + _____ pennies

 = _____ half dollars = _____ quarters = _____ dimes
= _____ nickels   = _____ pennies

 = _____ half dollars = _____ quarters = _____ dimes
= _____ nickels   = _____ pennies

3 **Find the sum and check.**

20	20	91	59	48	12	13	16
80	98	28	46	38	89	45	37
59	39	46	61	51	28	89	91
+ 19	+ 41	+ 32	+ 30	+ 52	+ 30	+ 32	+ 32

4. Draw a pictograph.

Transportation to School	Students
Walk	6
Bicycle	4
Bus	2
Car	8
Truck	3 ☆

each 🚶 represents 2 students

5. Solve the equations and check.

$n + 3 = (7 + 2) + 4$	$n + 5 = 3 + (6 + 1)$	$n + 8 = 5 + (8 + 0)$
check $10 + 3 = (7 + 2) + 4$ $10 + 3 = 9 + 4$ $13 = 13$	check	check

6. Find the product.

4,221 x 4	8,314 x 2	6,132 x 3	9,024 x 2	5,231 x 3	7,012 x 4	8,323 x 3

7. Write the missing numbers. Write the sum of all rows, columns, and diagonals.

3	8	1
2	4	6
7	0	5

_____

4	9	2
3	?	?
?	1	6

_____

6	?	2
?	8	?
14	?	10

_____

1 **Write the numbers.**

90¢ = _____ quarters + _____ dimes + _____ nickels + _____ pennies

67¢ = _____ quarters + _____ dimes + _____ nickels + _____ pennies

34¢ = _____ quarters + _____ dimes + _____ nickels + _____ pennies

85¢ = _____ quarters + _____ dimes + _____ nickels + _____ pennies

49¢ = _____ quarters + _____ dimes + _____ nickels + _____ pennies

21¢ = _____ quarters + _____ dimes + _____ nickels + _____ pennies

2 **Write < or >.**

24,286 ____ 38,157	91,640 ____ 91,460	46,198 ____ 46,189
53,725 ____ 56,275	75,432 ____ 75,342	82,537 ____ 82,535
61,375 ____ 61,735	81,649 ____ 86,149	23,476 ____ 23,467

3 **Solve the equations and check.**

$n + 4 = (7 + 1) + 5$	$n + 7 = 8 + (9 + 4)$	$n + 8 = (2 + 6) + 3$

4 **Find the product.**

X	5	1	9	6	0	8	3	7	2	4
8										
7										

113

Write the numbers.

38,156 is between _____ and 38,160 and is closer to _____.

94,072 is between _____ and 94,080 and is closer to _____.

65,485 is between _____ and 65,490 and is closer to _____.

42,697 is between _____ and 42,700 and is closer to _____.

83,154 is between _____ and 83,160 and is closer to _____.

6 **Find the sum and check.**

70	10	38	13	62	28	9	13
40	37	94	50	96	32	80	88
29	98	22	74	5	74	91	72
+ 19	+ 54	+ 1	+ 28	+ 15	+ 61	+ 17	+ 13

7 Amy bought 4 birthday cards. One cost $ 1.25, one $ 0.75, one $ 1.13, and one $ 2.47. How much did they cost? _____ Which cards could she buy if she only had $ 4.00? _____

Joe earned $ 2.50 by picking up Aunt Jan's newspaper while she was on vacation. Does he have enough to buy a kite priced at $ 1.85? ____ How much would he have left? _____ What coins would he receive as change? _____
_____

8 **Write the missing numbers. Write the sum of all rows, columns, and diagonals.**

5	11	?
?	6	?
10	?	7

6	?	4
?	7	?
10	?	?

?	?	3
?	6	7
9	?	?

_____   _____   _____

$$\begin{array}{r} {}^{2}28 \\ \times\ 3 \\ \hline 84 \end{array}$$

3 x 8 ones = 24 ones = 2 tens + 4 ones

put 4 in the ones' place, carry 2 tens to the tens' column

3 x 2 tens = 6 tens + 2 tens = 8 tens

$$\begin{array}{r} {}^{3}16 \\ \times\ 5 \\ \hline 80 \end{array}$$

5 x 6 ones = 30 ones = 3 tens + 0 ones

5 x 1 ten = 5 tens + 3 tens = 8 tens

(1) Find the product.

| $\begin{array}{r}{}^{1}27\\ \times\ 2\\ \hline 4\end{array}$ | $\begin{array}{r}35\\ \times\ 9\end{array}$ | $\begin{array}{r}12\\ \times\ 6\end{array}$ | $\begin{array}{r}39\\ \times\ 3\end{array}$ | $\begin{array}{r}23\\ \times\ 4\end{array}$ | $\begin{array}{r}28\\ \times\ 8\end{array}$ | $\begin{array}{r}14\\ \times\ 5\end{array}$ | $\begin{array}{r}16\\ \times\ 7\end{array}$ | $\begin{array}{r}25\\ \times\ 3\end{array}$ |

| $\begin{array}{r}24\\ \times\ 9\end{array}$ | $\begin{array}{r}38\\ \times\ 3\end{array}$ | $\begin{array}{r}13\\ \times\ 8\end{array}$ | $\begin{array}{r}27\\ \times\ 4\end{array}$ | $\begin{array}{r}32\\ \times\ 7\end{array}$ | $\begin{array}{r}45\\ \times\ 6\end{array}$ | $\begin{array}{r}49\\ \times\ 2\end{array}$ | $\begin{array}{r}16\\ \times\ 5\end{array}$ | $\begin{array}{r}36\\ \times\ 7\end{array}$ |

(2) Write < or >.

56¢ _____ 2 quarters + 1 dime + 1 nickel

84¢ _____ 2 quarters + 2 dimes + 2 nickels

38¢ _____ 1 quarter + 1 dime + 2 pennies

72¢ _____ 2 quarters + 1 dime + 4 pennies

47¢ _____ 1 quarter + 2 dimes + 2 nickels

63¢ _____ 1 quarter + 1 dime + 3 nickels + 3 pennies

(3) Find the sum and check.

23	13	18	14	37	60	23	29
81	92	48	61	52	47	83	16
69	43	90	84	60	25	18	33
+ 13	+ 17	+ 42	+ 37	+ 17	+ 31	+ 35	+ 90

4 **Write the numbers.**

25,473 is between _____ and _____ and is closer to _____.

73,698 is between _____ and _____ and is closer to _____.

87,217 is between _____ and _____ and is closer to _____.

48,365 is between _____ and _____ and is closer to _____.

32,972 is between _____ and _____ and is closer to _____.

69,524 is between _____ and _____ and is closer to _____.

5 **Solve the equations and check.**

$n + 5 = 9 + (2 + 7)$	$n + 6 = (4 + 8) + 5$	$n + 3 = 6 + (1 + 8)$

6 Sandy is 35 years old. How old will she be in 17 years? _____ _____ Will she be older or younger than 50? _____

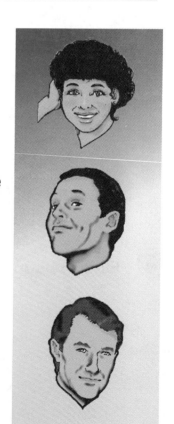

In 12 years Perry will be 45 years old. How old is he now? _____ _____ How old was he 10 years ago? _____ _____

Samuel is 14 years older than Joseph. Joseph is 32 years old. How old is Samuel? _____ _____ How old was Joseph 15 years ago? _____ _____

116

1 **Write the numbers.**

$1.34 = ___ dollars + ___ quarters + ___ dimes + ___ nickels + ___ pennies

$3.96 = ___ dollars + ___ quarters + ___ dimes + ___ nickels + ___ pennies

$2.19 = ___ dollars + ___ quarters + ___ dimes + ___ nickels + ___ pennies

$4.63 = ___ dollars + ___ quarters + ___ dimes + ___ nickels + ___ pennies

$0.82 = ___ dollars + ___ quarters + ___ dimes + ___ nickels + ___ pennies

$5.27 = ___ dollars + ___ quarters + ___ dimes + ___ nickels + ___ pennies

2 **Write the Roman numerals.**

66		92		35	
81		23		18	
44		79		57	
9		47		63	

3 **Find the difference and check.**

1,907	3,635	4,713	9,548	8,609	8,722	6,528
- 1,512	- 2,141	- 2,650	- 7,352	- 8,571	- 6,342	- 3,475

7,952	4,418	4,579	6,825	6,747	9,806	8,245
- 4,371	- 1,020	- 4,289	- 3,475	- 2,087	- 2,346	- 6,093

4 **Round the numbers to the nearest 10.**

18,432 ___	27,583 ___	40,258 ___	35,285 ___
56,799 ___	72,367 ___	65,674 ___	42,799 ___
93,145 ___	31,811 ___	84,926 ___	16,473 ___

⑤ Find the product.

95	22	53	46	26	58	44	85	37
x 4	x 7	x 8	x 4	x 8	x 9	x 7	x 6	x 3

35	64	15	32	72	43	16	73	48
x 7	x 9	x 9	x 6	x 9	x 6	x 9	x 7	x 8

⑥ Write = or ≠.

7 x 9 _____ 63	7 x 6 _____ 48	8 x 9 _____ 64
8 x 4 _____ 24	7 x 3 _____ 21	7 x 5 _____ 35
7 x 7 _____ 48	8 x 6 _____ 48	7 x 8 _____ 54
7 x 2 _____ 14	8 x 8 _____ 72	7 x 4 _____ 28

⑦ Write +, -, or x.

and	_____	more than	_____	difference	_____
left	_____	times	_____	altogether	_____
less than	_____	in all	_____	sum	_____
product	_____	both	_____	minus	_____
plus	_____	take away	_____		

⑧

Dana is reading a book of 400 pages. How many pages are there in $\frac{1}{2}$ of the book? _____ _____ If Dana has read 222 pages, has she read more or less than half of the book? _____

Greg ate $\frac{1}{4}$ of the pizza. Louisa ate $\frac{1}{3}$ of the pizza. Which child ate the most pizza? (Draw a picture if necessary.)

1 **Match the figure to its description.**

A solid with all edges the same size and all faces the same size.

A round smooth figure with all points a given distance from the center.

Four-sided figure with four square corners

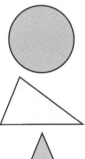

A solid with a flat round base and narrows to a point at the top.

Three-sided figure with three angles.

2 **Write <, >, or =.**

13 ___ XII	54 ___ XXXIV	76 ___ XLVI
91 ___ XCI	28 ___ XXXVIII	67 ___ LXXVI
45 ___ XIV	89 ___ LXXXIX	33 ___ XXXIII

3 **Find the difference and check.**

| 7,961 | 7,814 | 8,238 | 6,915 | 7,903 | 8,546 | 4,854 |
| - 5,470 | - 1,583 | - 7,071 | - 4,694 | - 5,861 | - 7,293 | - 2,380 |

| 1,922 | 3,718 | 6,409 | 6,845 | 8,634 | 5,963 | 5,426 |
| - 1,682 | - 3,260 | - 6,134 | - 2,360 | - 6,054 | - 5,282 | - 1,394 |

④ Round the numbers to the nearest 10.

34,186 _____	42,694 _____	67,472 _____	31,204 _____
81,848 _____	28,331 _____	13,717 _____	75,898 _____
50,253 _____	95,069 _____	76,525 _____	64,915 _____

⑤ Find the sum.

46 + 100 = _____	16,826 + 100 = _____	978 + 100 = _____
5,173 + 100 = _____	86 + 100 = _____	792 + 100 = _____
354 + 100 = _____	6,234 + 100 = _____	81,541 + 100 = _____

⑥ Write + or -.

The girls sold how many candy bars altogether? _____

Keith has how many more baseball cards than Kyle? _____

There were how many pictures in all? _____

What is the difference of 12 and 7? _____

Joyce had how many less books than Don? _____

Paul and James had how many tomatoes? _____

What is eighteen plus twelve? _____

How many students were left? _____

⑦ Find the product.

46	34	23	29	66	34	83	12	94
x 2	x 8	x 4	x 7	x 7	x 3	x 9	x 8	x 6

15	52	48	76	74	58	67	99	78
x 8	x 5	x 3	x 6	x 4	x 7	x 5	x 5	x 5

1 Write the equivalent fractions.

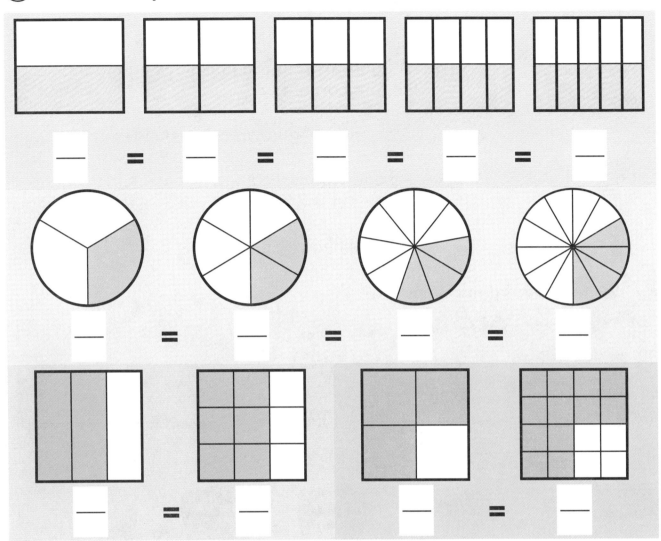

2 Write the Arabic numbers.

XXVI _____   LXXIV _____   LXVIII _____

XLIX _____   XLI _____   LXXXVII _____

LIII _____   LXXXV _____   LXII _____

3 Find the difference and check.

9,718	9,736	9,587	8,928	8,754	9,208	3,725
- 8,645	- 1,084	- 3,197	- 2,761	- 8,393	- 5,094	- 1,482

4 **Match the figure to its description.**

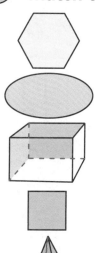

A solid with two parallel bases and all rectangular faces.

A figure with four equal sides and four square corners.

A six-sided figure with equal sides.

A solid with a rectangular base narrowing to a point at the top.

A squashed circle.

5 **Write the word numbers.**

$\frac{1}{10}$ = 0.1 = _____ $\frac{4}{10}$ = 0.4 = _____

$\frac{6}{10}$ = 0.6 = _____ $\frac{9}{10}$ = 0.9 = _____

6 **Write the numbers.**

1 bushel = ____ pecks

1 peck   = ____ gallons

7 **Measure the lines with an inch ruler.**

____ _____

____ _____

1 **Circle the sets. Write the division fact.**

sets of 4

12 ÷ 4 = ___

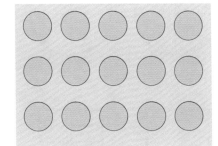

sets of 3

_____

sets of 2

_____

sets of 5

_____

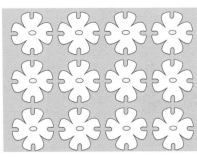

sets of 3

_____

sets of 4

_____

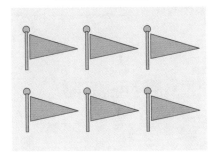

sets of 2

_____

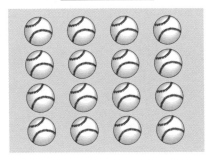

sets of 4

_____

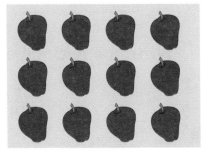

sets of 2

_____

2 **Write one addition and one multiplication word problem. Find the answers.**

_____   _____

_____   _____

_____   _____

_____   _____

③ Write the equivalent fractions.

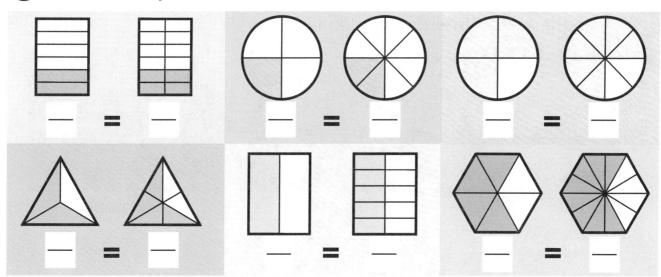

--- = ---   --- = ---   --- = ---

--- = ---   --- = ---   --- = ---

④ Unscramble the names of the shapes or solids.

hagonex _____   tonacog _____   lircce _____

buce _____   glaniter _____   dircleny _____

sheper _____   mipardy _____   once _____

loav _____   gnatcleer _____   searqu _____

⑤ Write the decimal equivalent.

$\frac{4}{10}$ = _____ $\frac{6}{10}$ = _____ $\frac{8}{10}$ = _____ $\frac{5}{10}$ = _____

$\frac{7}{10}$ = _____ $\frac{3}{10}$ = _____ $\frac{1}{10}$ = _____ $\frac{2}{10}$ = _____

⑥ Write the numbers.

1 bushel = ____ pecks   1 peck = ____ gallons

⑦ Write <, >, or =.

19 ____ XXIX   27 ____ XXVII   84 ____ LXXXIV

36 ____ XXXVI   58 ____ LXXXV   43 ____ XLI

72 ____ LXII   95 ____ XLI   61 ____ LXVI

1 **Write the numbers.**

36,872 has a _____ in the tens' place.

36,872 has a _____ in the thousands' place.

36,872 has a _____ in the ones' place.

36,872 has a _____ in the ten thousands' place.

36,872 has a _____ in the hundreds' place.

2 **Draw and circle the given sets. Write the division fact.**

20 squares	24 triangles	18 circles
sets of 2	sets of 3	sets of 3
_____	_____	_____
18 kites	8 trapezoids	13 diamonds
sets of 6	sets of 2	sets of 13
_____	_____	_____

3 **Circle the correct number of units needed.**

125

4. Shade the equivalent fraction. Write the fractions.

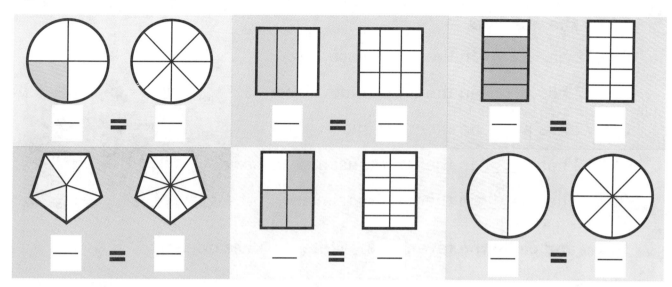

—— = ——   —— = ——   —— = ——

—— = ——   —— = ——   —— = ——

5. Find the sum and check.

311	421	310	723	144	262	247	364
620	215	419	339	227	215	827	604
607	138	220	201	802	608	511	213
+ 249	+ 902	+ 837	+ 415	+ 314	+ 811	+ 103	+ 702

6. Match the figure to its description.

Five-sided figure with equal sides.

The shape of a ball.

Solid with two parallel circular bases and round smooth sides.

Four-sided figure with equal sides and not square corners.

Figure with eight equal sides.

7. Write +, -, or x.

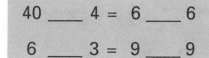

40 ___ 4 = 6 ___ 6   8 ___ 3 = 6 ___ 4   4 ___ 4 = 8 ___ 8

6 ___ 3 = 9 ___ 9   5 ___ 3 = 20 ___ 5   16 ___ 8 = 4 ___ 2

1 Write the numbers.

(3 + 6) + 8 = ____ + (____ + ____)   (7 + 2) + 5 = ____ + (____ + ____)

2 + (9 + 4)= (____ + ____) + ____   6 + (2 + 0)= (____ + ____) + ____

(1 + 7) + 4 = ____ + (____ + ____)   3 + (8 + 5)= (____ + ____) + ____

2 Write the equivalent fractions that are shaded.

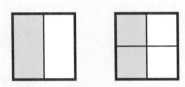 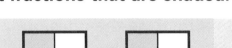 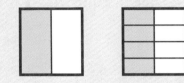

numerator is x by ____   numerator is x by ____   numerator is x by ____

denominator is x by ____   denominator is x by ____   denominator is x by ____

 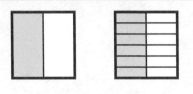 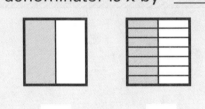

numerator is x by ____   numerator is x by ____   numerator is x by ____

denominator is x by ____   denominator is x by ____   denominator is x by ____

3 Write multiplicand, product, denominator, multiplier, or numerator.

$\frac{1}{2}$ _____   6 _____

_____   x 8 _____

48 _____

4 Write even or odd.

789 _____	4,526 _____	43 _____
5,371 _____	62 _____	217 _____
58 _____	835 _____	1,694 _____

5 **Write the numbers.**

49,150 has a ____ in the hundreds' place.

49,150 has a ____ in the ones' place.

49,150 has a ____ in the ten thousands' place.

49,150 has a ____ in the tens' place.

49,150 has a ____ in the thousands' place.

6 **Draw a picture to demonstrate the division fact. Find the answers.**

$12 \div 3 =$ ____	$6 \div 3 =$ ____	$9 \div 3 =$ ____
$8 \div 4 =$ ____	$10 \div 2 =$ ____	$15 \div 3 =$ ____

7 **Find the sum. Write the terms.**

```
  920      _____
  311      _____
  233      _____
+ 484      _____
           _____
```

143	421	242	812	654
961	193	822	803	372
52	721	282	152	831
+ 822	+ 431	+ 222	+ 91	+ 210

8 At the hardware store, Dick saw 7 bins of nails. The clerk told him there were 1,000 nails in each bin. How many nails were in the 7 bins?

Sherry, Mandy, and Tammy guessed they weighed about 350 pounds altogether. If Sherry weighed 114 pounds, Mandy 136 pounds, and Tammy 98 pounds, how much did the girls weigh? ____ _____ Was their guess a good estimate? ____

128

1 **Write the correct time.** 10 pts. total for this exercise.

_____ _____ _____ _____ _____

_____ _____ _____ _____ _____

2 **Find the product.** 9 pts. total for this exercise.

| 128 x 2 | 104 x 5 | 139 x 3 | 228 x 4 | 117 x 6 | 113 x 5 | 249 x 2 | 217 x 4 | 108 x 6 |

3 **Write the numbers.** 16 pts. total for this exercise.

7 + (8 + 5) = (____ + ____) + 5   (4 + 3) + 2 = ____ + (3 + ____)
____ + ____ = ____ + ____   ____ + ____ = ____ + ____
____ = ____   ____ = ____

4 **Write the numbers.** 25 pts.

$0.69 = ____ dollars + ____ quarters + ____ dimes + ____ nickels + ____ pennies

$0.75 = ____ dollars + ____ quarters + ____ dimes + ____ nickels + ____ pennies

$1.42 = ____ dollars + ____ quarters + ____ dimes + ____ nickels + ____ pennies

$0.58 = ____ dollars + ____ quarters + ____ dimes + ____ nickels + ____ pennies

$3.17 = ____ dollars + ____ quarters + ____ dimes + ____ nickels + ____ pennies

(5) Draw a pictograph. 5 pts. total for this exercise.

Ice Cream Cones Sold

Vanilla   24
Strawberry   16
Chocolate   20
Peach   4
Butter Pecan 8

each 🍦 equals 4.

(6) Solve the equations. 3 pts. total for this exercise.

n + 3 = (5 + 2) + 7	n + 7 = 3 + (6 + 4)	n + 8 = (5 + 4) + 7

(7) Find the sum and check. 8 pts. total for this exercise.

30	21	29	12	12	69	28	13
20	21	10	39	19	14	24	28
19	28	37	20	13	2	12	23
+ 29	+ 26	+ 11	+ 26	+ 52	+ 11	+ 23	+ 12

(8) Write the Roman numerals. 12 pts. total for this exercise.

36 _____	28 _____	15 _____
74 _____	62 _____	89 _____
83 _____	40 _____	9 _____
51 _____	4 _____	97 _____

88 Total pts.

1 **Write ones', tens', hundreds', thousands', or ten thousands'.**

67,135   The 1 is in the _____ place.

The 5 is in the _____ place.

The 7 is in the _____ place.

The 3 is in the _____ place.

The 6 is in the _____ place.

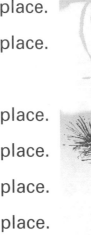

28,409   The 8 is in the _____ place.

The 0 is in the _____ place.

The 4 is in the _____ place.

The 2 is in the _____ place.

The 9 is in the _____ place.

2 **Write the division fact demonstrated.**

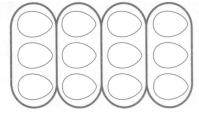 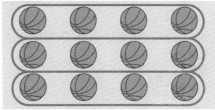 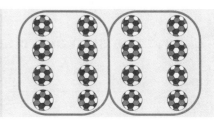

____ ÷ ____ = ____   ____ ÷ ____ = ____   ____ ÷ ____ = ____

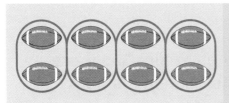 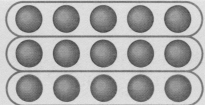 

____ ÷ ____ = ____   ____ ÷ ____ = ____   ____ ÷ ____ = ____

3 **Color the even numbers blue and the odd numbers red.**

165   542   390   427   879   653   934   286   391

4 **Add 100 to each number.**

47,315 _____   7,857 _____   83 _____   3,519 _____

56 _____   138 _____   9,270 _____   80,248 _____

442 _____   59,673 _____   665 _____   24 _____

5 **Write the equivalent fractions.**

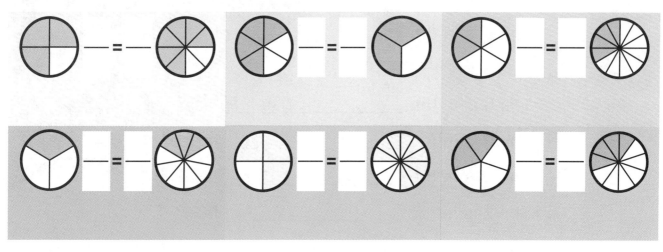

The top number is the _____ .

The bottom number is the _____ .

6 **Find the sum and check. Write the terms.**

$1.75	_____	$2.52	$1.61	$1.41	$1.64	$4.71
0.27	_____	3.63	1.64	2.35	2.26	1.36
1.53	_____	1.11	5.09	2.37	3.34	0.58
+6.31	_____	+1.29	+1.20	+3.72	+1.42	+2.14
	_____					

7 Brett has 624 pennies in his bank. If his daddy gave him 100 more pennies to put in his bank, how many pennies will he have in his bank?

Frank rode 2,469 miles with his family on a trip. If they only have 100 more miles to go, how far will they have traveled?

Becky had 3,286 stamps in her stamp collection. If she gave 100 of them to Brenda, how many stamps did she have left?

132

1 Find the product. Write the terms.

406 x 3	_____ _____	308 x 5	509 x 8	801 x 7	603 x 4	907 x 9	506 x 6

_____

206 x 2	504 x 3	207 x 7	609 x 5	706 x 2	305 x 6	508 x 4	403 x 8	704 x 7

2 Write the division fact two other ways. Find the answer.

$56 \div 7 = $ _____ $\dfrac{56}{7} = $ $7\overline{)56}$

$42 \div 6 = $ _____

_____   _____

_____ $\dfrac{45}{9} = $ _____

_____ $\dfrac{18}{3} = $ _____

_____   _____ $6\overline{)12}$

_____   _____ $4\overline{)28}$

3 Write the numbers.

$4 \times 12 = 4 \times (2 + 10) = (4 \times 2) + (4 \times 10) = \underline{8} + \underline{40} = \underline{48}$

$6 \times 13 = 6 \times (\underline{} + 10) = (6 \times \underline{}) + (6 \times 10) = \underline{} + \underline{60} = \underline{}$

$3 \times 16 = 3 \times (6 + \underline{}) = (\underline{} \times 6) + (3 \times 10) = \underline{18} + \underline{} = \underline{}$

$8 \times 14 = \underline{} \times (4 + 10) = (8 \times \underline{}) + (\underline{} \times 10) = \underline{} + \underline{} = \underline{}$

$5 \times 18 = \underline{} \times (8 + \underline{}) = (\underline{} \times 8) + (\underline{} \times 10) = \underline{} + \underline{} = \underline{}$

133

4 Shade and write the equivalent fraction.

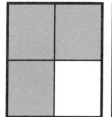  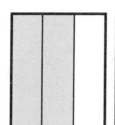  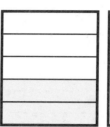 

$\dfrac{3}{4}$ $\dfrac{3 \times 2}{4 \times 2} =$ — $\dfrac{2}{3}$ $\dfrac{2 \times 3}{3 \times 3} =$ — $\dfrac{2}{5}$ $\dfrac{2 \times 2}{5 \times 2} =$ —

 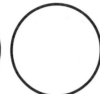 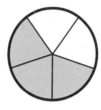 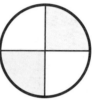 

$\dfrac{2}{6}$ $\dfrac{2 \times 2}{6 \times 2} =$ — $\dfrac{3}{5}$ $\dfrac{3 \times 2}{5 \times 2} =$ — $\dfrac{2}{4}$ $\dfrac{2 \times 3}{4 \times 3} =$ —

5 Draw a bar graph.

Pounds of Aluminum Gathered by
the Students

Andrea	8 lbs.
Jessica	12 lbs.
Amy	7 lbs.
Jenny	14 lbs.
Greg	10 lbs.

6 Find the difference.

5,726	6,149	8,633	5,375	5,297	7,586	9,474
- 3,915	- 1,729	- 5,731	- 3,940	- 4,301	- 2,635	- 2,721

7 If Billy has 4 red balls and 6 green balls, what fractional part of all his balls are red? _____ What fractional part of all his balls are green? _____

134

divisor 8$\overline{)24}$ $\overset{3}{}$ quotient / dividend

Quotient is the answer in division.

Divisor is the number by which you are dividing.

Dividend is the number into which you are dividing.

_____ 3$\overline{)27}$ $\overset{9}{}$ _____
_____

1 Write the division fact two other ways. Find the answer.

$35 \div 7 =$ ____

_____ _____

_____ $\frac{18}{2} =$ _____

_____ _____ 4$\overline{)24}$

_____ $\frac{32}{8} =$ _____

$63 \div 7 =$ ____

_____ _____ 6$\overline{)54}$

2 Write the numbers.

$2 \times 17 = 2 \times ($___$ + 10) = (2 \times 7) + (2 \times$ ___$) =$ ___$+$ ___$=$ ____

$6 \times 15 =$ ___$\times (5 + 10) = (6 \times$ ___$) + (6 \times 10) =$ ___$+$ ___$=$ ____

$8 \times 12 = 8 \times (2 +$ ___$) = ($___$\times 2) + ($___$\times 10) =$ ___$+$ ___$=$ ____

$9 \times 11 =$ ___$\times (1 + 10) = (9 \times$ ___$) + (9 \times$ ___$) =$ ___$+$ ___$=$ ____

$3 \times 14 = 3 \times ($___$+$ ___$) = (3 \times$ ___$) + (3 \times$ ___$) =$ ___$+$ ___$=$ ____

$5 \times 13 =$ ___$\times (3 +$ ___$) = ($___$\times 3) + ($___$\times 10) =$ ___$+$ ___$=$ ____

135

3 Draw a bar graph.

Choose five people you know from five different families.

4 Find the product.

600	400	800	200	700	300	500	900	400
x 7	x 3	x 5	x 9	x 4	x 8	x 6	x 5	x 8

302	806	105	601	203	504	407	709	608
x 9	x 3	x 7	x 5	x 4	x 8	x 7	x 6	x 8

5 Find the difference and check.

7,061	9,484	2,539	5,376	6,588	3,487	8,245
- 5,260	- 7,732	- 1,801	- 1,623	- 618	- 734	- 5,912

6 Write two subtraction word problems. Use the key words " left" and "more than."

_____   _____

_____   _____

_____   _____

_____   _____

(1) Write < or >.

eighty-four thousand, three hundred seventy-three ____ 84,365

fifty-two thousand, six hundred three ____ 52,703

thirty-seven thousand, four hundred sixteen ____ 37,415

ninety-three thousand, one hundred eighty-four ____ 92,184

twenty-six thousand, five hundred twenty-seven ____ 26,627

seventy-five thousand, two hundred ninety-eight ____ 75,299

(2) Circle the answers that are incorrect and correct them.

3,213	1,319	3,125	3,224	1,323	4,107	1,822
1,824	2,421	2,927	3,620	2,912	1,512	3,627
1,431	1,622	1,730	1,723	3,417	934	2,305
+ 2,419	+ 2,534	+ 1,015	+ 1,017	+ 1,126	+ 3,223	+ 1,011
8,887	7,996	8,797	9,484	8,778	9,776	8,865

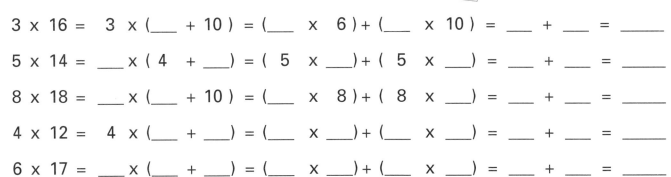

(3) Write the numbers.

3 x 16 = 3 x (___ + 10) = (___ x 6) + (___ x 10) = ___ + ___ = _____

5 x 14 = ___ x (4 + ___) = (5 x ___) + (5 x ___) = ___ + ___ = _____

8 x 18 = ___ x (___ + 10) = (___ x 8) + (8 x ___) = ___ + ___ = _____

4 x 12 = 4 x (___ + ___) = (___ x ___) + (___ x ___) = ___ + ___ = _____

6 x 17 = ___ x (___ + ___) = (___ x ___) + (___ x ___) = ___ + ___ = _____

(4) Find the difference and check.

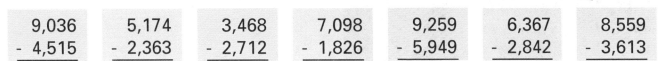

9,036	5,174	3,468	7,098	9,259	6,367	8,559
- 4,515	- 2,363	- 2,712	- 1,826	- 5,949	- 2,842	- 3,613

5 Write the division terms.

```
        9  _____
    4 ) 36  _____
```

_____

_____ 20 ÷ 4 = 5 _____

$$\frac{18}{2} = 9$$ _____

Write the division facts two other ways. Find the quotient.

54 ÷ 9 = ____   _____   _____

_____ $$\frac{72}{8} =$$ _____

_____   _____   3) 18

6 Find the product.

4,070	6,080	9,050	3,020	7,010	6,030	8,050
x 6	x 7	x 5	x 8	x 4	x 9	x 3

7 Match the terms.

100 years	before Christ
B.C.	decade
1,000 years	anno Domini
A.D.	millennium
10 years	century

1 to A.D. 99	– 1st century
A.D. 100 to A.D. 199	– 2nd century
A.D. 200 to A.D. 299	– 3rd century
A.D. 300 to A.D. 399	– 4th century
A.D. 400 to A.D. 499	– 5th century
↓	↓
A.D. 1600 to A.D. 1699	– 17th century
A.D. 1700 to A.D. 1799	– 18th century
A.D. 1800 to A.D. 1899	– 19th century
A.D. 1900 to A.D. 1999	– 20th century
A.D. 2000 to A.D. 2099	– 21st century

1 **Write the numbers.**

1 pound (lb.) = 16 ounces (oz.)   1 ton (T) = 2,000 pounds (lbs.)

_____ weighs about an ounce.

_____ weighs about a pound.

_____ weighs about a ton.

1 T   = ____ lbs.   1 lb. = ____ oz.

2 **Find the product.**

$60.03	$50.08	$ 30.02	$70.01	$ 40.09	$60.02	$ 40.07
x 5	x 8	x 6	x 4	x 7	x 8	x 4

3,008	5,040	7,000	2,006	9,080	6,001	3,050
x 7	x 4	x 5	x 9	x 3	x 5	x 9

3 **Write the division terms.**

$$6\overline{)24} \quad \frac{4}{} \qquad \text{_____}$$

_____

$$\frac{32}{8} = 4 \qquad \text{_____}$$

_____   21 ÷ 3 = 7   _____

Write the division facts two other ways. Find the quotient.

$$\frac{40}{8} =$$

_____   _____

$$3\overline{)12}$$

_____   _____

4 Write < or >.

twenty-one thousand, seven hundred fifty-seven ____ 21,857

fifty-eight thousand, three hundred ninety-two ____ 58,394

fifteen thousand, sixty-four ____ 14,064

twenty-nine thousand, two hundred ten ____ 79,230

forty-six thousand, four hundred eighty-three ____ 46,583

5 Write the numbers.

2 x 14 = 2 x (__ + __) = (2 x __)+ (2 x __) = __ + __ = ____

6 x 12 = __ x (__ + __) = (__ x __)+ (__ x __) = __ + __ = ____

5 x 16 = __ x (__ + __) = (__ x __)+ (__ x __) = __ + __ = ____

9 x 17 = __ x (__ + __) = (__ x __)+ (__ x __) = __ + __ = ____

4 x 15 = __ x (__ + __) = (__ x __)+ (__ x __) = __ + __ = ____

7 x 18 = __ x (__ + __) = (__ x __)+ (__ x __) = __ + __ = ____

6 Find the sum and check.

1,712	3,271	2,815	1,426	3,204	1,733	3,354
1,322	1,692	1,052	1,480	1,761	2,172	1,212
2,341	1,412	2,080	1,722	2,180	1,021	960
+ 3,192	+ 2,021	+ 1,720	+ 1,320	+ 1,733	+ 2,842	+ 2,431

7 Add 100 to each number.

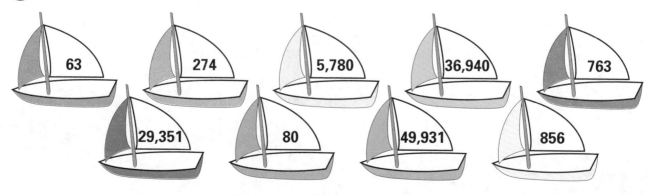

63   274   5,780   36,940   763

29,351   80   49,931   856

140

1 How much money is left from $10.00?

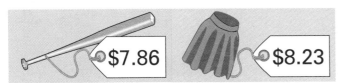  

$7.86 $8.23 $1.35 $4.57

_____   _____   _____   _____

Write the number of bills and coins received as change.

____ dollar bills ____ quarters ____ dimes ____ nickels ____ pennies

____ dollar bills ____ quarters ____ dimes ____ nickels ____ pennies

____ dollar bills ____ quarters ____ dimes ____ nickels ____ pennies

____ dollar bills ____ quarters ____ dimes ____ nickels ____ pennies

2 Write the division facts two other ways. Find the quotient.

$\dfrac{72}{8}$ =   _____   _____

_____ $4\overline{)24}$ _____

_____ $2\overline{)10}$ _____

_____   _____ $16 \div 4 =$ ___

$\dfrac{18}{6}$ =   _____   _____

_____   _____ $12 \div 6 =$ ___

141

3   Add 100 to each number.

| 49,672 | 547 | 5,983 | 23 | 8,061 | 438 |

4   Write the numbers.

1 lb. = ____ oz.   1 ton = ____ pounds

5   Find the sum and check.

$ 12.81	$ 13.30	$ 23.35	$ 42.39	$ 16.20	$ 24.43	$ 54.94
21.54	22.60	20.95	3.26	0.81	3.78	3.16
31.27	10.58	21.34	31.30	21.29	0.07	10.35
+ 13.05	+ 12.29	+ 20.12	+ 1.81	+ 0.29	+ 1.21	+ 1.12

6   Write the numbers.

3 x 23 = 3 x (3 + 20) = (3 x ___)+ (3 x ___) = ___ + ___ = _____

7 x 25 = 7 x (5 + ___) = (7 x ___)+ (___ x ___) = ___ + ___ = _____

5 x 28 = 5 x (___ + ___) = (___ x 8)+ (___ x ___) = ___ + ___ = _____

8 x 27 = ___ x (___ + ___) = (___ x ___)+ (___ x ___) = ___ + ___ = _____

4 x 24 = ___ x (___ + ___) = (___ x ___)+ (___ x ___) = ___ + ___ = _____

7   Using the single digit numbers only once, the three circles in a straight line must add up to:

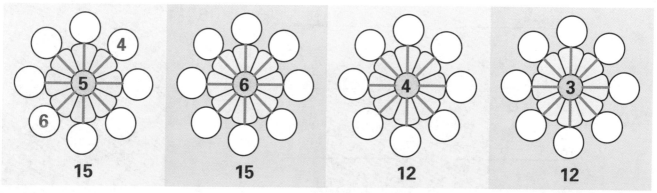

| 15 | 15 | 12 | 12 |

1 Write in expanded and standard form. Place commas where needed.

40000 + 7000 + 300 + 60 + 2 =
(   ) + (   ) + (   ) + (   ) + (   ) = _____

50000 + 9000 + 100 + 80 + 7 =
(   ) + (   ) + (   ) + (   ) + (   ) = _____

80000 + 3000 + 500 + 20 + 4 =
(   ) + (   ) + (   ) + (   ) + (   ) = _____

20000 + 6000 + 900 + 10 + 8 =
(   ) + (   ) + (   ) + (   ) + (   ) = _____

70000 + 5000 + 800 + 30 + 6 =
(   ) + (   ) + (   ) + (   ) + (   ) = _____

2 How much money is left from $ 5.00?

 $3.47    $2.75    $1.89    $4.23

_____   _____   _____   _____

What change would you receive?

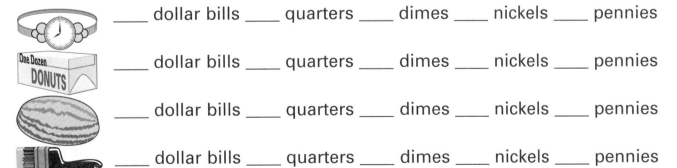

____ dollar bills ____ quarters ____ dimes ____ nickels ____ pennies

____ dollar bills ____ quarters ____ dimes ____ nickels ____ pennies

____ dollar bills ____ quarters ____ dimes ____ nickels ____ pennies

____ dollar bills ____ quarters ____ dimes ____ nickels ____ pennies

3 Write the equivalents.

16 oz. = 1 _____   2,000 pounds = 1 _____

143

(4) Round the numbers to the nearest 100.

8,386 is between 8,300 and _____ but is closer to _____.

3,754 is between 3,700 and _____ but is closer to _____.

7,291 is between 7,200 and _____ but is closer to _____.

4,905 is between 4,900 and _____ but is closer to _____.

2,462 is between 2,400 and _____ but is closer to _____.

5,837 is between 5,800 and _____ but is closer to _____.

(5) Write 1 multiplication fact and 2 division facts.

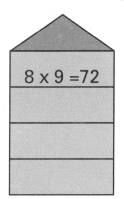 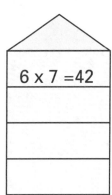 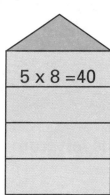 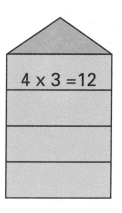

8 x 9 = 72   6 x 7 = 42   5 x 8 = 40   4 x 3 = 12

(6) Write +, -, or x.

2 ____ 9 = 9 ____ 9

15 ____ 3 = 4 ____ 3

4 ____ 4 = 9 ____ 7

5 ____ 2 = 16 ____ 6

12 ____ 3 = 4 ____ 5

7 ____ 3 = 16 ____ 5

(7) Find the quotient.

4)36   3)21   5)45   7)70   9)45   8)72

7)42   9)18   6)30   2)18   6)54   10)90

(8) Danny had a half dollar, 2 dimes, and 4 nickels. How much money does he have? _____ If he spent $0.64, how much does he have left? _____

144

1 **Solve the equations.**

n + 6 = (2 x 4) + 5	n + 3 = (5 x 2) + 2	n + 8 = (4 x 6) - 10
n + 5 = (7 x 5) + 10	n + 9 = (8 x 3) - 14	n + 4 = 5 x (8 - 6)

2 **Write 1 multiplication fact and 2 division facts.**

9 x 3 = 27   7 x 5 = 35   8 x 4 = 32   6 x 2 = 12

3 **Find the quotient.**

$6\overline{)36}$ $8\overline{)64}$ $7\overline{)28}$ $8\overline{)72}$ $4\overline{)20}$ $8\overline{)16}$

$5\overline{)40}$ $4\overline{)32}$ $4\overline{)40}$ $2\overline{)16}$ $3\overline{)27}$ $5\overline{)20}$

25 ÷ 5 = ___   27 ÷ 9 = ___   54 ÷ 6 = ___   9 ÷ 1 = ___   8 ÷ 2 = ___

4 How much money is left from $15.00?

_____   _____   _____   _____

5 Write in expanded and standard form.

30,000 + 80 + 200 + 5 + 7,000 =
(   ) + (   ) + (   ) + (   ) + (   ) = _____

600 + 7 + 1,000 + 90 + 40,000 =
(   ) + (   ) + (   ) + (   ) + (   ) = _____

2,000 + 30 + 80,000 + 500 + 4 =
(   ) + (   ) + (   ) + (   ) + (   ) = _____

50 + 9,000 + 100 + 60,000 + 8 =
(   ) + (   ) + (   ) + (   ) + (   ) = _____

2 + 300 + 4,000 + 70 + 90,000 =
(   ) + (   ) + (   ) + (   ) + (   ) = _____

6 Round the numbers to the nearest 100.

2,864 is between _____ and 2,900 but is closer to _____.

5,379 is between _____ and 5,400 but is closer to _____.

1,642 is between _____ and 1,700 but is closer to _____.

3,957 is between _____ and 4,000 but is closer to _____.

7 Find the difference and check.

9,590	5,273	6,192	6,045	8,381	3,464	7,876
- 6,936	- 649	- 2,403	- 4,316	- 7,647	- 749	- 3,928

$$\begin{array}{r} \overset{1}{56} \\ \times\ 3 \\ \hline 168 \end{array}$$ 3 x 6 ones = 18 ones = 1 ten + 8 ones (carry the 1 ten)

3 x 5 tens + 1 ten = 15 tens + 1 ten = 16 tens = 1 hundred + 6 tens

(1) Find the product.

27	75	59	45	69	63	37	98	36
x 7	x 2	x 8	x 5	x 4	x 2	x 9	x 8	x 4

86	97	37	49	55	74	26	87	58
x 3	x 2	x 4	x 9	x 3	x 6	x 5	x 3	x 7

(2) Trace the outline of the shapes and solids. Write their names.

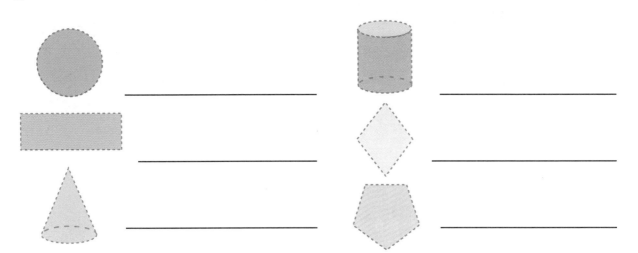

(3) Round the numbers to the nearest 100.

63,875 is between _____ and _____ but is closer to _____.

49,210 is between _____ and _____ but is closer to _____.

98,561 is between _____ and _____ but is closer to _____.

37,402 is between _____ and _____ but is closer to _____.

84,623 is between _____ and _____ but is closer to _____.

51,749 is between _____ and _____ but is closer to _____.

4 Write 1 multiplication and 2 division facts.

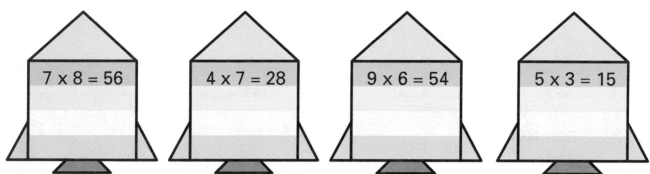

| 7 x 8 = 56 | 4 x 7 = 28 | 9 x 6 = 54 | 5 x 3 = 15 |

5 Write in expanded and standard form.

7,000 + 80 + 30,000 + 200 + 5 =
(   ) + (   ) + (   ) + (   ) + (   ) = _____

600 + 90 + 40,000 + 1,000 + 7 =
(   ) + (   ) + (   ) + (   ) + (   ) = _____

30 + 4 + 2,000 + 500 + 80,000 =
(   ) + (   ) + (   ) + (   ) + (   ) = _____

60,000 + 50 + 9,000 + 8 + 100 =
(   ) + (   ) + (   ) + (   ) + (   ) = _____

6 Solve the equations.

| n + 7 = (2 x 8) - 3 | n + 5 = (4 x 6) + 1 | n + 8 = (3 x 5) + 10 |

7 Find the difference and check.

| 7,241 | 8,056 | 7,192 | 4,874 | 9,280 | 6,383 | 5,465 |
| - 1,902 | - 2,749 | - 3,584 | - 1,905 | - 3,759 | - 5,527 | - 2,938 |

148

1 **Round the numbers to the nearest 100.**

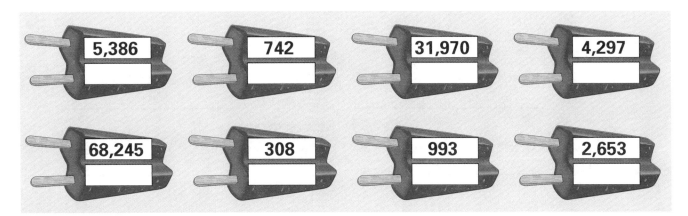

| 5,386 | 742 | 31,970 | 4,297 |
| 68,245 | 308 | 993 | 2,653 |

2 **Find the product.**

| 78 | 82 | 67 | 95 | 52 | 43 | 43 | 36 | 29 |
| x 5 | x 2 | x 8 | x 3 | x 4 | x 3 | x 7 | x 9 | x 4 |

| 68 | 27 | 74 | 68 | 76 | 59 | 24 | 32 | 45 |
| x 7 | x 9 | x 4 | x 3 | x 2 | x 5 | x 5 | x 8 | x 7 |

3 **Find the quotient.**

6)48   3)18   2)8   5)35   9)90   7)56

4)12   8)40   9)81   8)24   3)15   9)36

4)28   8)32   3)6   3)30   2)14   6)12

8)48   6)42   9)54   5)45   7)28   4)32

4 Trace the outline of the shapes and solids. Write their names.

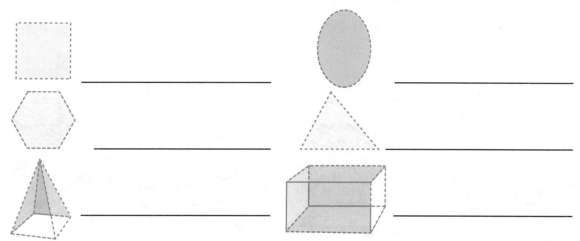

_____

_____

_____

_____

_____

_____

5 Write in expanded and standard form.

30,000 + 1,000 + 500 + 50 + 2 =
(   ) + (   ) + (   ) + (   ) + (   ) = _____

70 + 2,000 + 100 + 40,000 + 5 =
(   ) + (   ) + (   ) + (   ) + (   ) = _____

200 + 60,000 + 4 + 90 + 4,000 =
(   ) + (   ) + (   ) + (   ) + (   ) = _____

9,000 + 300 + 80,000 + 7 + 80 =
(   ) + (   ) + (   ) + (   ) + (   ) = _____

6 Find the difference.

| $ 62.97 | $ 91.66 | $ 55.81 | $ 80.44 | $ 33.70 | $ 46.32 | $ 82.53 |
| - 55.78 | - 18.07 | - 28.73 | - 38.29 | - 27.54 | - 19.04 | - 37.28 |

7 Cindy went to a birthday party at 10:00 A.M. She stayed for 3 hours. What time was it when she came home?

Jimmy went to sleep at 8:30 P.M. He was awakened by a thunder storm at 2:30 A.M. How many hours had he been asleep? _____ _____ If he wanted to sleep 9 hours, at what time should his mother wake him? _____

1 **Add 100 to each number.** 4 pts. total for this exercise.

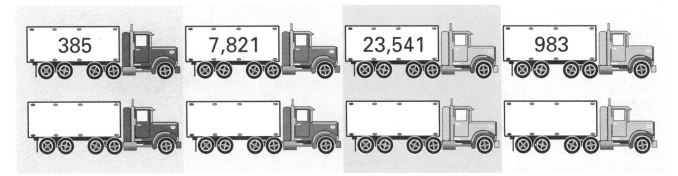

385   7,821   23,541   983

2 **Find the difference.** 7 pts. total for this exercise.

| 4,365
- 2,839 | 7,398
- 4,623 | 6,458
- 5,939 | 8,749
- 1,250 | 9,291
- 5,629 | 5,837
- 2,694 | 7,413
- 2,086 |

3 **Match the figure to its name.** 16 pts. total for this exercise.

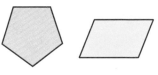

square
rectangle
oval
pentagon
octagon
trapezoid
sphere
cone

circle
triangle
diamond
hexagon
parallelogram
cube
cylinder
pyramid

4 **Write even or odd.** 9 pts. total for this exercise.

63 _____	19 _____	5,374 _____
150 _____	8,486 _____	45 _____
792 _____	238 _____	6,827 _____

5 The students did the following number of push ups on track and field day: Sam 26, Ross 44, Abel 107, Betty 79, Cody 9. Together they did how many push ups? 1 pt.

Jody had 3 boxes of crayons with 24 in each box. How many crayons did Jody have in all? 1 pt.

6 **Circle the given sets. Write the division facts.** 3 pts. total for this exercise.

sets of 2   sets of 3   sets of 3

_____   _____   _____

7 **Write the division facts 2 other ways.** 6 pts. total for this exercise.

30 ÷ 6 = 5   _____   _____

_____ $\frac{18}{2} = 9$ _____

_____   _____ $6\overline{)54}$ with 9 above

1 **Write the correct time.**

_____ _____ _____ _____ _____

2 **Round the numbers to the nearest 100.**

| 436 | 87,780 | 7,547 | 163 | 8,271 |

3 **Find the product.**

45	72	58	29	87	32	93	64	70
x 6	x 3	x 4	x 6	x 3	x 7	x 6	x 2	x 9

4 **Write the equivalent fractions.**

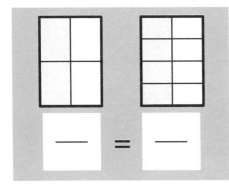 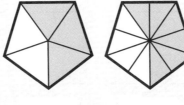 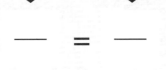 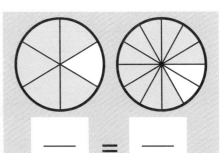

___ = ___   ___ = ___   ___ = ___

153

5 Trace the outline of the shapes and solids. Write their names.

_____

_____

_____

_____

6 Find the sum. Write the terms.

64	_____
1	_____
4	_____
10	_____
+ 63	_____
	_____

71	32	20	70	61
33	54	54	18	37
22	44	26	94	2
11	5	63	2	10
+ 38	+ 30	+ 15	+ 12	+ 74

63	60	41	83	16	14	61	13
24	25	25	16	42	71	32	61
44	73	92	20	32	23	27	5
31	24	10	75	33	20	50	82
+ 4	+ 15	+ 17	+ 1	+ 62	+ 69	+ 16	+ 26

7 Write two subtraction word problems using A.M. and P.M. Find the answers.

_____   _____

_____   _____

_____   _____

_____   _____

① **Write the numbers.**

53,672 has a ____ in the hundreds' place.

63,431 has a ____ in the ten thousands' place.

42,296 has a ____ in the tens' place.

71,198 has a ____ in the thousands' place.

94,525 has a ____ in the ones' place.

② **Write the correct time.**

_____ _____ _____ _____ _____

_____ _____ _____ _____ _____

③ **Write < or >.**

95,127 ____ 95,684	27,951 ____ 27,915	52,719 ____ 52,791
83,064 ____ 83,061	34,386 ____ 32,386	46,843 ____ 46,847
68,430 ____ 64,830	71,295 ____ 71,925	19,572 ____ 29,572

④ **Round the numbers to the nearest dollar.**

$ 6.43 ____	$ 23.57 ____	$ 36.95 ____	$ 78.21 ____
$ 10.64 ____	$ 51.82 ____	$ 87.38 ____	$ 45.76 ____

5 Shade the equivalent fractions. Write the fractions.

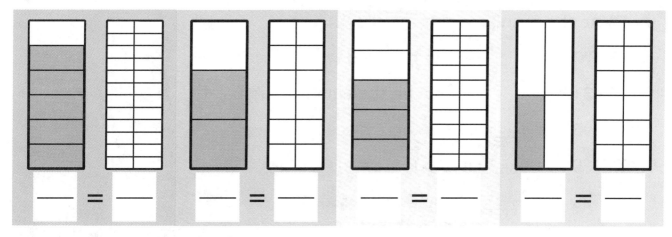

— = —   — = —   — = —   — = —

6 Solve the equations.

n + 3 = 6 + (2 x 6)	n + 5 = 3 + (4 x 6)	n + 8 = 5 + (7 x 2)

7 Find the sum and check. Write the terms.

```
  68    _____      12    53    24    27    18
  11    _____      15    21    70    56    60
  23    _____      62    10    37    43    17
  30    _____      51    44    31    41    21
+ 51    _____    + 46  + 38  + 22  + 20  + 60
        _____
```

8 Find the product.

```
  70      52      83      44      39      37      20      69      78
x  4    x  2    x  5    x  6    x  4    x  6    x  8    x  2    x  3


  76      86      67      27      98      48      95      58      83
x  6    x  5    x  8    x  7    x  6    x  5    x  2    x  8    x  9
```

156

(1) Write the standard numbers.

forty-five thousand, one hundred twenty-seven _____

eighty-four thousand, three hundred eighty-six _____

sixty-two thousand, seven hundred nineteen _____

thirteen thousand, sixty-four _____

twenty-seven thousand, nine hundred fifty-one _____

ninety-eight thousand, four hundred thirty _____

seventy-one thousand, two hundred ninety-five _____

fifty-six thousand, eight hundred forty-three _____

(2) Solve the equations.

n + 6 = 8 + (3 x 5)	n + 2 = 6 + (4 x 5)	n + 7 = 3 + (2 x 8)

(3) Shade the equivalent fraction. Write the fractions.

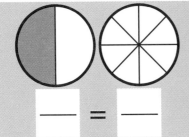

___ = ___

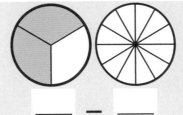

___ = ___

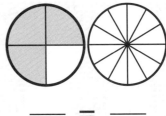

___ = ___

numerator is x by ____   numerator is x by ____   numerator is x by ____

denominator is x by ____   denominator is x by ____   denominator is x by ____

The top number in a fraction is called the _____ .

The bottom number in a fraction is called the _____ .

(4) Write the correct time.

_____ _____ _____ _____ _____

(5) Write the numbers.

24,084 has a ____ in the thousands' place.

84,091 has a ____ in the tens' place.

61,976 has a ____ in the hundreds' place.

43,685 has a ____ in the ones' place.

27,182 has a ____ in the ten thousands' place.

(6) Find the product.

88	63	30	45	59	94	73	52	64
x 9	x 2	x 6	x 8	x 0	x 9	x 3	x 9	x 7

(7) Write < or >.

36,157 ____ 27,158	59,347 ____ 59,345	87,561 ____ 87,651
18,026 ____ 18,260	42,890 ____ 40,289	28,409 ____ 28,431

(8) Find the sum and check.

19	11	10	61	83	25	11	12
18	12	71	62	81	50	31	44
10	8	41	10	9	29	32	34
80	93	17	16	22	61	94	51
+ 61	+ 52	+ 28	+ 19	+ 1	+ 20	+ 28	+ 36

158

1 Draw the hands on the face of the clocks.

5:47   11:12   12:36   3:53   8:22

2 Write the value of the red digit in word numbers.

43,786 _____

29,501 _____

58,234 _____

90,167 _____

35,879 _____

3 Write the equivalent fractions. Write the terms for $\frac{3}{4}$.

$\frac{3}{4} = \frac{3 \times 4}{4 \times 4} = $ ____ $\frac{2}{3} = \frac{2 \times 6}{3 \times 6} = $ ____ $\frac{2}{5} = \frac{2 \times 5}{5 \times 5} = $ ____

$\frac{3}{4} = $ ____ $\frac{2}{3} = $ ____ $\frac{2}{5} = $ ____

$\frac{1}{4} = \frac{1 \times 7}{4 \times 7} = $ ____ $\frac{5}{6} = \frac{5 \times 3}{6 \times 3} = $ ____ $\frac{3}{8} = \frac{3 \times 3}{8 \times 3} = $ ____

____ = ____   ____ = ____   ____ = ____

$\frac{1}{3} = \frac{1 \times 8}{3 \times 8} = $ ____ $\frac{3}{5} = \frac{3 \times 4}{5 \times 4} = $ ____ $\frac{5}{8} = \frac{5 \times 2}{8 \times 2} = $ ____

____ = ____   ____ = ____   ____ = ____

159

4 **Draw a line graph.**

Games Joe Won as a Pitcher

1988	10
1989	15
1990	9
1991	13
1992	20
1993	17

5 **Find the sum and check.**

21	17	80	61	10	36	50	50
13	13	34	53	14	24	72	95
32	53	25	14	45	10	13	10
8	22	4	24	26	52	25	15
+ 91	+ 92	+ 16	+ 27	+ 92	+ 53	+ 16	+ 18

6 **Find the product.**

65	72	24	86	93	55	37	48	57
x 4	x 7	x 7	x 4	x 6	x 9	x 4	x 9	x 8

7 **Write the words on the right in the correct blanks.**

A _____ is 100 years.   B.C.

_____ stands for before Christ.   decade

A _____ is 1,000 years.   millennium

A _____ is 10 years.   A.D.

_____ stands for *in the year of the Lord.*   century

1950 is in the _____ century.   20th

1 Write = or ≠.

$\frac{2}{3}$ ___ $\frac{4}{6}$	$\frac{3}{4}$ ___ $\frac{9}{12}$	$\frac{2}{5}$ ___ $\frac{6}{10}$	$\frac{4}{6}$ ___ $\frac{16}{24}$
$\frac{1}{4}$ ___ $\frac{3}{16}$	$\frac{3}{5}$ ___ $\frac{12}{20}$	$\frac{1}{6}$ ___ $\frac{4}{18}$	$\frac{1}{4}$ ___ $\frac{6}{14}$

2 Write 1 multiplication and 2 division facts.

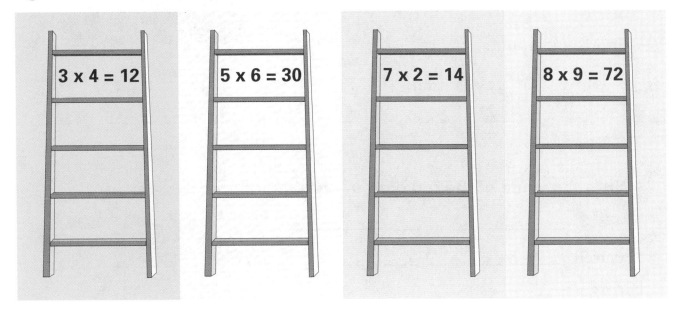

3 x 4 = 12   5 x 6 = 30   7 x 2 = 14   8 x 9 = 72

3 Find the quotient.

$4\overline{)24}$ $7\overline{)21}$ $3\overline{)9}$ $2\overline{)4}$ $5\overline{)30}$ $3\overline{)12}$

$8\overline{)80}$ $5\overline{)15}$ $2\overline{)6}$ $3\overline{)24}$ $7\overline{)14}$ $8\overline{)56}$

4 Find the difference and check.

9,567	7,654	6,333	9,291	8,170	5,182	6,395
- 6,729	- 6,808	- 3,804	- 5,889	- 5,635	- 2,536	- 1,947

5 **Draw a line graph.**

Choose five people you
know and graph the
number of pets they own.

6 **Find the product.**

80	75	97	58	27	38	47	65	76
x 7	x 5	x 2	x 6	x 9	x 5	x 3	x 2	x 4

7 **Write the value of the red digit in word numbers.**

74,253 _____

80,169 _____

26,784 _____

53,091 _____

47,628 _____

8 Fred had finished $\frac{1}{4}$ of his homework and Gil had finished $\frac{5}{16}$. Write
the equivalent fraction for $\frac{1}{4}$ with a denominator of 16. _____ Have the
boys finished the same amount of homework? _____ Which boy had
completed the most homework? _____

Write a fraction that has a 4 in the numerator and a 9 in the
denominator.

$$\frac{2}{3} \searrow \frac{4}{6} \qquad \frac{2}{3} \nearrow \frac{4}{6} \qquad \frac{2}{3} = \frac{4}{6}$$

2 x 6 = 12 · · · · · 3 x 4 = 12 · · · · · 12 = 12

$$\frac{2}{5} \searrow \frac{4}{9} \qquad \frac{2}{5} \nearrow \frac{4}{9} \qquad \frac{2}{5} \neq \frac{4}{9}$$

2 x 9 = 18 · · · · · 5 x 4 = 20 · · · · · 18 ≠ 20

1 Write = or ≠.

$$\frac{2}{4} \ \square \ \frac{3}{6} \qquad \frac{4}{8} \ \square \ \frac{5}{10} \qquad \frac{1}{3} \ \square \ \frac{3}{6} \qquad \frac{2}{5} \ \square \ \frac{3}{8}$$

_____   _____   _____   _____

_____   _____   _____   _____

2 Find the product.

64	86	72	49	53	95	34	28	61
x 9	x 8	x 9	x 6	x 3	x 7	x 6	x 8	x 4

3 Write 2 multiplication facts and 2 division facts.

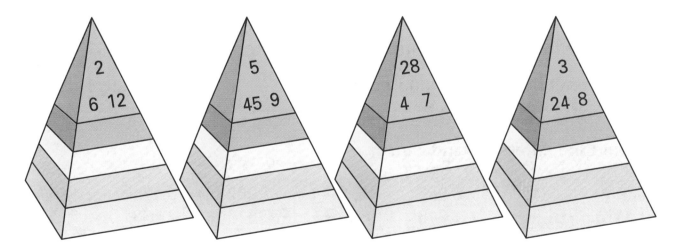

2 6 12   5 45 9   28 4 7   3 24 8

4 Denise had 9 crayons in her desk. She gave 4 of them to Doris. What part of her crayons did she give to Doris? _____ What part of her crayons did she have left? _____

Keith had 6 balloons. 2 of them popped. What part of his balloons popped? _____ What part of his balloons did he have left? _____

5 Find the quotient. Write the terms.

_____ 2$)\overline{10}$ _____

6$)\overline{24}$ 4$)\overline{28}$ 7$)\overline{35}$ 9$)\overline{72}$ 3$)\overline{21}$ 8$)\overline{48}$

3$)\overline{18}$ 2$)\overline{14}$ 5$)\overline{45}$ 4$)\overline{16}$ 6$)\overline{36}$ 5$)\overline{20}$

6 Write = or ≠.

sixty-three thousand, eight hundred seventy-three	____	63,783
twenty-nine thousand, five hundred forty-two	____	29,542
ninety-six thousand, one hundred eight	____	96,108
seventy-two thousand, ninety-five	____	72,950
fifty-four thousand, three hundred seventy	____	54,307
eighteen thousand, six hundred fifty-four	____	18,654

7 Find the difference and check.

9,390	3,486	8,055	5,473	7,362	6,274	4,547
- 2,541	- 1,669	- 1,218	- 3,849	- 2,517	- 2,658	- 1,829

1 List each measurement under one of the following groups:
inch, pint, gallon, ton, cup, foot, pound, yard, quart

liquid	linear	weight
_____	_____	_____
_____	_____	_____
_____	_____	
_____		

2 Write = or ≠.

$\frac{1}{2}$ ☐ $\frac{4}{10}$ $\frac{3}{5}$ ☐ $\frac{6}{10}$ $\frac{2}{3}$ ☐ $\frac{6}{9}$ $\frac{1}{4}$ ☐ $\frac{4}{15}$

_____   _____   _____   _____

_____   _____   _____   _____

3 Find the difference and check. Write the terms.

$\begin{array}{r} 8,721 \\ - 4,916 \end{array}$ _____
   _____
   _____

$\begin{array}{r} 5,561 \\ - 2,603 \end{array}$ $\begin{array}{r} 6,074 \\ - 4,756 \end{array}$ $\begin{array}{r} 7,280 \\ - 1,943 \end{array}$ $\begin{array}{r} 9,195 \\ - 4,728 \end{array}$

4 Write 2 multiplication and 2 division facts.

165

5

Find the quotient. Write the terms.

_____   4$\overline{)8}$ _____
                              _____

| 9$\overline{)72}$ | 5$\overline{)35}$ | 3$\overline{)24}$ | 4$\overline{)28}$ | 8$\overline{)40}$ | 4$\overline{)36}$ |

| 7$\overline{)21}$ | 6$\overline{)48}$ | 9$\overline{)54}$ | 2$\overline{)18}$ | 2$\overline{)8}$ | 9$\overline{)18}$ |

(6) **Write the numbers.**

3 x 18 = 3 x (8 + ___) = (3 x ___)+ (3 x 10) = 24 + ___ = _____

4 x 13 = ___ x (___ + ___) = (___ x ___)+ (___ x ___) = ___ + ___ = _____

8 x 17 = ___ x (___ + ___) = (___ x ___)+ (___ x ___) = ___ + ___ = _____

7 x 16 = ___ x (___ + ___) = (___ x ___)+ (___ x ___) = ___ + ___ = _____

5 x 14 = ___ x (___ + ___) = (___ x ___)+ (___ x ___) = ___ + ___ = _____

(7) **Write < or >.**

twenty-five thousand, two hundred seventy-six	____	25,267
sixty-three thousand, eight hundred nine	____	63,890
twenty thousand, four hundred fifty-seven	____	19,457
forty-eight thousand, twenty-six	____	48,260
fifty-four thousand, three hundred seventy	____	54,584

(8) **Measure the lines with a 12 inch ruler.**

___ _____

___ _____

___ _____

1 **Write the distance from:**

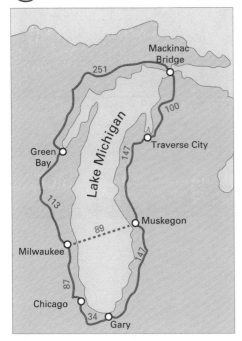

Chicago to Milwaukee _____ _____

Green Bay to Milwaukee _____ _____

Muskegon to Gary _____ _____

Mackinac Bridge to Traverse City _____ _____

Gary to Chicago _____ _____

Traverse City to Muskegon _____ _____

Mackinac Bridge to Green Bay _____ _____

Milwaukee to Muskegon going

across the lake _____ _____

2 **Write the numbers.**

2 x 29 = 2 x (9 + 20) = (___ x ___)+ (___ x ___) = ___ + ___ = _____

6 x 28 = ___ x (___ + ___) = (___ x ___)+ (___ x ___) = ___ + ___ = _____

4 x 26 = ___ x (___ + ___) = (___ x ___)+ (___ x ___) = ___ + ___ = _____

8 x 23 = ___ x (___ + ___) = (___ x ___)+ (___ x ___) = ___ + ___ = _____

3 x 24 =

3 **Find the difference and check. Write the terms.**

$ 92.43   _____
- 38.17   _____
            _____

$ 60.91 $ 96.80 $ 84.71 $ 71.65
- 25.78   - 18.29   - 67.35   - 47.38

4 **Write linear, liquid, or weight.**

pound _____   yard _____   gallon _____

inch _____   cup _____   foot _____

quart _____   ton _____   pint _____

5 Write = or ≠.

$$\frac{3}{4} \;\square\; \frac{9}{8} \qquad\qquad \frac{1}{2} \;\square\; \frac{6}{12} \qquad\qquad \frac{3}{5} \;\square\; \frac{9}{15} \qquad\qquad \frac{1}{6} \;\square\; \frac{5}{36}$$

_____ _____ _____ _____

_____ _____ _____ _____

6 Find the product.

908	413	928	607	812	938	904	716	512
x 7	x 4	x 3	x 6	x 4	x 2	x 8	x 7	x 6

7 Write the decimal equivalent and word number.

$\frac{3}{10}$ _____ = _____ $\frac{2}{10}$ _____ = _____

$\frac{5}{10}$ _____ = _____ $\frac{7}{10}$ _____ = _____

$\frac{8}{10}$ _____ = _____ $\frac{4}{10}$ _____ = _____

8 Find the product. Write even or odd.

```
  6   _____        5   _____
x 8   _____      x 9   _____
      _____            _____


  9   _____        4   _____
x 2   _____      x 8   _____
      _____            _____


  7   _____        7   _____
x 4   _____      x 3   _____
      _____            _____
```

168

1 **Write the distance from:**

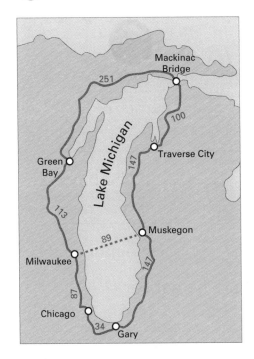

Chicago to Muskegon _____ _____

Traverse City to Gary _____ _____

Green Bay to Chicago _____ _____

Milwaukee to Mackinac Bridge _____ _____

Mackinac Bridge to Chicago _____ _____

Milwaukee to Traverse City

crossing the lake _____ _____

Green Bay to Traverse City _____ _____

Gary to Mackinac Bridge _____ _____

2 **Write the Roman numerals.**

C = 100	CD = 400	D = 500	CM = 900	M = 1,000

386 _____

475 _____

721 _____

549 _____

134 _____

652 _____

298 _____

913 _____

867 _____

3 **Find the sum and check.**

```
    1        6        6        0        7        7        5        3
    6        8        3        6        8        8        3        8
    6        7        9        7        1        2        8        6
    7        4        7        3        2        8        2        0
  + 3      + 2      + 6      + 9      + 7      + 3      + 7      + 9
```

169

④ $3.69 $9.19 $6.46

$4.39 $2.89 $1.78

Kenneth has $10.00 to go shopping. What three items could he buy?

_____

How much would he have left if he bought the book? _____ Could he buy

the mini car and the basketball? _____ Why or why not?_____

What would the ping pong paddle, top, and jacks cost? _____ How much

change would he get? _____ What bills and coins would he get back?

_____

⑤ **Write the fractional equivalent and word number.**

0.6 = _____ = _____ 0.3 = _____ = _____

0.1 = _____ = _____ 0.8 = _____ = _____

0.7 = _____ = _____ 0.2 = _____ = _____

⑥ **Write inches, feet, or yards as the unit of measure.**

book _____   plywood _____   football field_____

picnic table _____   pencil _____   screw driver _____

room _____   yard goods _____   window _____

⑦ **Measure the lines with a 12 inch ruler.**

___ _____

___ _____

1 Write the bills and coins received as change if paid for with $5.00.

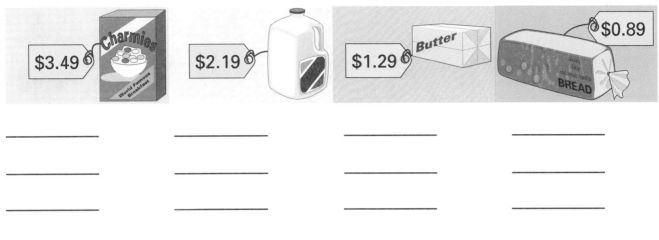

$3.49 $2.19 $1.29   Butter   BREAD $0.89

_____   _____   _____   _____

_____   _____   _____   _____

_____   _____   _____   _____

_____   _____   _____   _____

2 Write cup, pint, quart, or gallon as the unit of measure for each.

coffee _____   motor oil _____

strawberries _____   gasoline _____

milk _____   cream _____

ice cream _____   tea _____

3 Write the Roman numerals.

C = 100	CD = 400	D = 500	CM = 900	M = 1,000

547 _____   962 _____   203 _____

184 _____   438 _____   721 _____

609 _____   895 _____   356 _____

4 Write even or odd.

93,451 _____   56,348 _____   47,125 _____

34,786 _____   12,913 _____   69,872 _____

78,264 _____   85,637 _____   21,590 _____

5 Find the sum and check.

9	5	1	1	6	4	3	2
8	4	9	3	0	2	2	8
3	9	5	5	9	8	9	7
4	6	4	8	9	8	1	1
+ 2	+ 1	+ 5	+ 9	+ 2	+ 6	+ 7	+ 1

6 Write the numbers.

8 x 23 = 8 x (3 + 20) = (___ x ___)+ (___ x ___) = ___ + ___ = _____

2 x 25 = ___ x (___ + ___) = (___ x ___)+ (___ x ___) = ___ + ___ = _____

7 x 27 =

6 x 21 =

3 x 26 =

5 x 28 =

4 x 24 =

7 Find the product.

629	218	416	917	526	603	824	315	704
x 4	x 6	x 5	x 5	x 3	x 9	x 3	x 7	x 8

8 Sherri picked 8 quarts of strawberries. She could fit 4 quarts into a gallon jar. How many gallon jars did she need?

Shawn measured the four sides of the backyard to be 16 yards, 18 yards, 16 yards, and 18 yards. If he wanted to fence in the backyard, how many yards of fencing would he need?

172

1 **Shade the equivalent fractions.** 3 pts. total for this exercise.

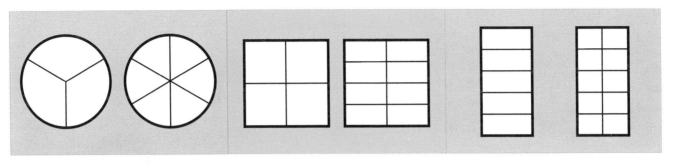

$\dfrac{2}{3} = \dfrac{4}{6}$ $\dfrac{1}{4} = \dfrac{2}{8}$ $\dfrac{3}{5} = \dfrac{6}{10}$

2 **Round the numbers to the nearest 100.** 8 pts. total for this exercise.

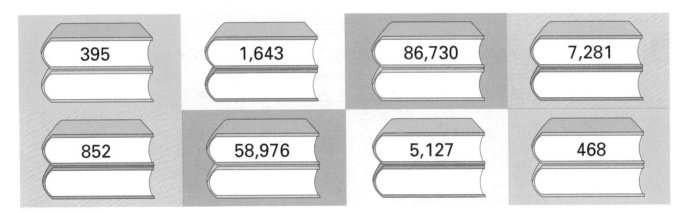

395   1,643   86,730   7,281

852   58,976   5,127   468

3 Catherine gave the clerk $10.00 to buy a blouse priced at $7.39. How much money did she receive back from the clerk? _____ What bills and coins would the clerk give her? _____

_____ 2 pts.

4 **Write < or >.** 4 pts. total for this exercise.

four thousand, one hundred fifty-three	____	4,135
eight thousand, three hundred seventy-two	____	8,327
two thousand, five hundred ninety-four	____	2,549
six thousand, seven hundred eight	____	6,780

173

5 **Find the product.** 9 pts. total for this exercise.

46	38	79	64	53	86	26	37	85
x 9	x 7	x 2	x 4	x 4	x 7	x 3	x 5	x 6

6 **Write the numbers.** 5 pts. total for this exercise.

72,654 has a ____ in the hundreds' place.

81,914 has a ____ in the tens' place.

63,872 has a ____ in the thousands' place.

23,659 has a ____ in the ones' place.

41,286 has a ____ in the ten thousands' place.

7 **Write ones', tens', hundreds', thousands', or ten thousands'.** 5 pts.

13,980   The 3 is in the _____ place.

The 8 is in the _____ place.

The 1 is in the _____ place.

The 9 is in the _____ place.

The 0 is in the _____ place.

8 **Find the sum.** 8 pts. total for this exercise.

12	10	22	20	11	31	11	35
51	91	10	11	32	27	17	60
83	64	16	28	48	27	23	2
14	16	89	76	92	41	41	87
+ 29	+ 16	+ 40	+ 60	+ 13	+ 60	+ 94	+ 14

44 Total pts.

174

1 **Write the bills and coins received as change if paid for with $10.00.**

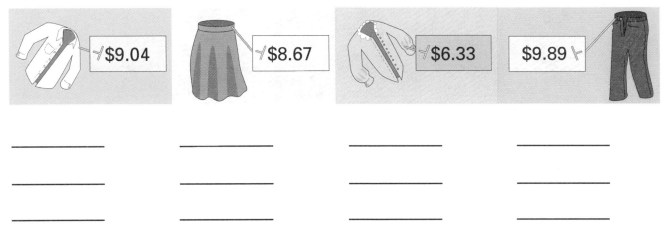

$9.04 $8.67 $6.33 $9.89

_____   _____   _____   _____

_____   _____   _____   _____

_____   _____   _____   _____

_____   _____   _____   _____

2 **Find the product.**

$ 7.15	$ 8.22	$ 2.13	$ 8.37	$ 4.29	$ 5.02	$ 3.05	$ 6.16
x 7	x 4	x 8	x 2	x 3	x 9	x 6	x 5

3 **Write the decimal and fraction equivalents.**

six-tenths = _____ = _____   five-tenths = _____ = _____

one-tenth = _____ = _____   three-tenths = _____ = _____

nine-tenths = _____ = _____   eight-tenths = _____ = _____

4 **Write the Arabic numbers.**

CCCXXIV _____   CCXCVIII _____

DXXXVI _____   CMLXVII _____

DCCCLXXI _____   CDXII _____

DCLIII _____   DCCXLV _____

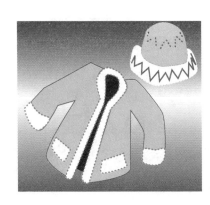

175

5 Find the sum.

2	7	1	6	2	7	4	6
8	5	9	4	8	3	8	9
6	4	5	8	9	9	6	3
3	7	6	5	1	4	9	1
+ 7	+ 3	+ 7	+ 5	+ 9	+ 8	+ 2	+ 1

6 Write the numbers.

3 x 24 = ___ x (___ + ___) = (___ x ___)+ (___ x ___) = ___ + ___ = _____

7 x 23 =

4 x 21 =

9 x 28 =

2 x 26 =

6 x 29 =

5 x 27 =

8 x 25 =

7 Write two word problems using English linear measurements.

_____   _____

_____   _____

_____   _____

_____   _____

_____   _____